Discovering Algebra

An Investigative Approach

Teaching and Worksheet Masters

Key Curriculum Press
Innovators in Mathematics Education

Teacher's Materials Project Editor: Elizabeth DeCarli

Project Administrator: Aaron Madrigal

Project Management: Rozi Harris, Interactive Composition Corporation

Copyeditor: Victoria P. Thulman

Editorial Production Supervisor: Christine Osborne

Production Director: McKinley Williams

Production Coordinator: Ann Rothenbuhler

Text Designer: Jenny Somerville

Composition, Technical Art, Prepress: Interactive Composition Corporation

Cover Designers: Jill Kongabel, Marilyn Perry

Printer: Alonzo Printing

Textbook Product Manager: James Ryan

Executive Editor: Casey FitzSimons

Publisher: Steven Rasmussen

Cover Photo Credits: Background image: Pat O'Hara/DRK Photo. Boat image: Marc Epstein/DRK Photo. All other images: Ken Karp Photography.

Key Curriculum Press
1150 65th Street
Emeryville, CA 94608
(510) 595-7000
editorial@keypress.com
www.keypress.com

Printed in the United States of America
10 9 8 7 6 5 4 3 2 09 08 07 06

ISBN-13: 978-1-55953-766-7
ISBN-10: 1-55953-766-3

Contents

Chapter 8

Chapter 9

Chapter 10

Chapter 11

Graph Paper

Introduction

These masters for *Discovering Algebra: An Investigative Approach* are designed for your students to use as they work on investigations or projects, or for you to use in your classroom presentations and discussions. The *Discovering Algebra Teacher's Edition* lists the masters by lesson in the introduction before the beginning of each chapter, as well as in the materials list at the beginning of each lesson.

Transparency masters contain graphs and diagrams from the student text, enlarged so that they can be seen easily when displayed on an overhead projector. Worksheet masters are designed to help students perform investigations or work on special projects. Some masters can be used for both transparencies and worksheets. If a worksheet is required for an investigation, it is listed in the student text and in the materials list in the margin of the *Teacher's Edition.* Optional worksheet masters are listed only in the *Teacher's Edition* and are followed by the word *optional.*

The masters are listed for the first lesson in which they appear. Some, such as the Coordinate Plane transparency, may be used with many different lessons. Masters for several different sizes of graph paper are also included; these may be used in a variety of ways.

Connect the Dots

Name ______________________________ Period __________ Date ______________

Stage 1

Stage 2

Stage 3

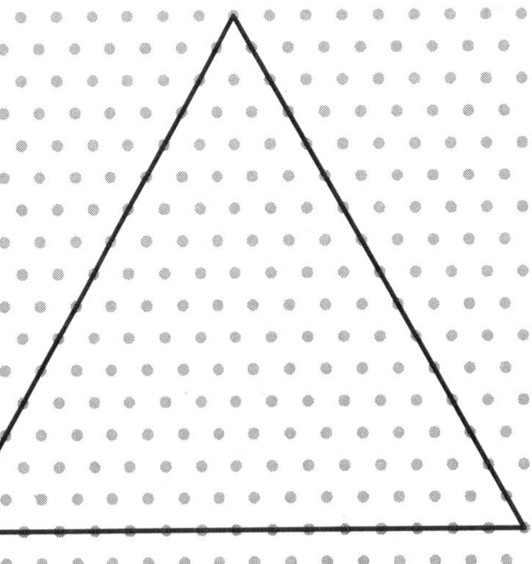

Stage 4

How Many?

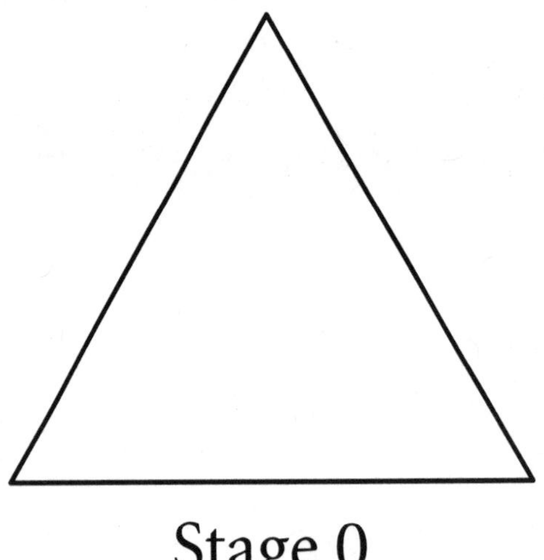

Stage 0

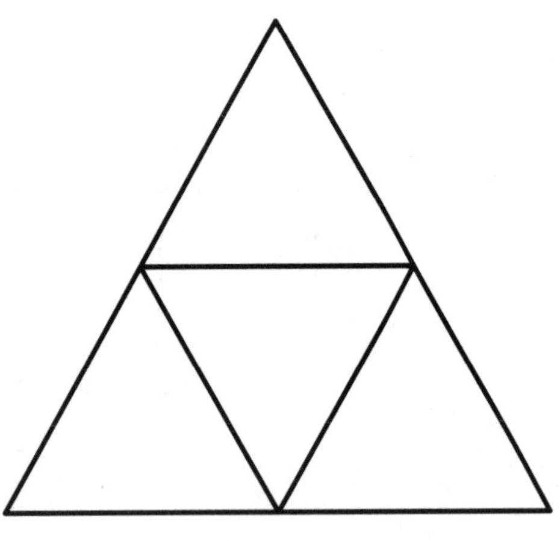

Stage 1

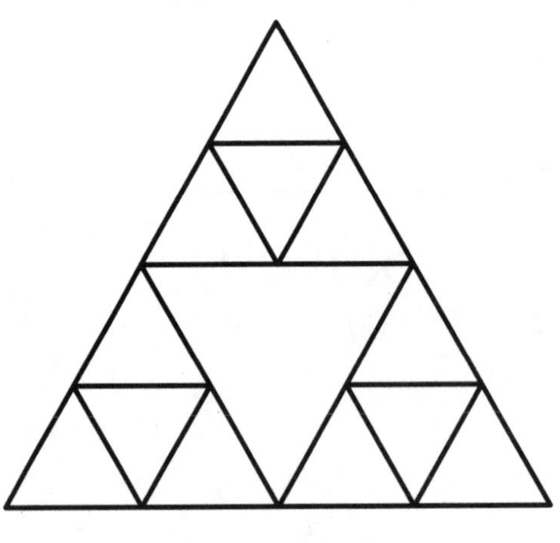

Stage 2

Stage 3

Stage 4

How Long Is This Fractal?

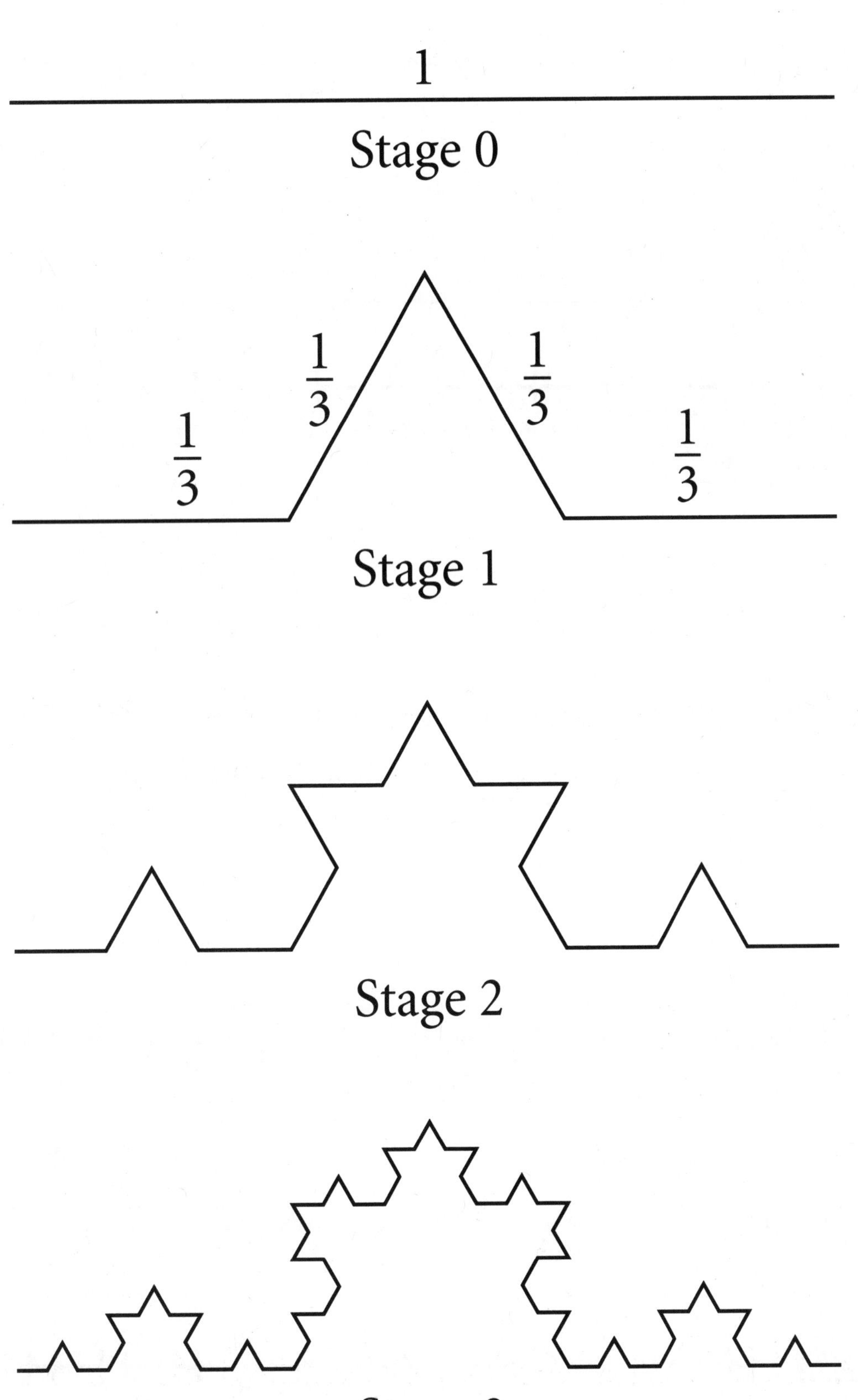

Number Lines

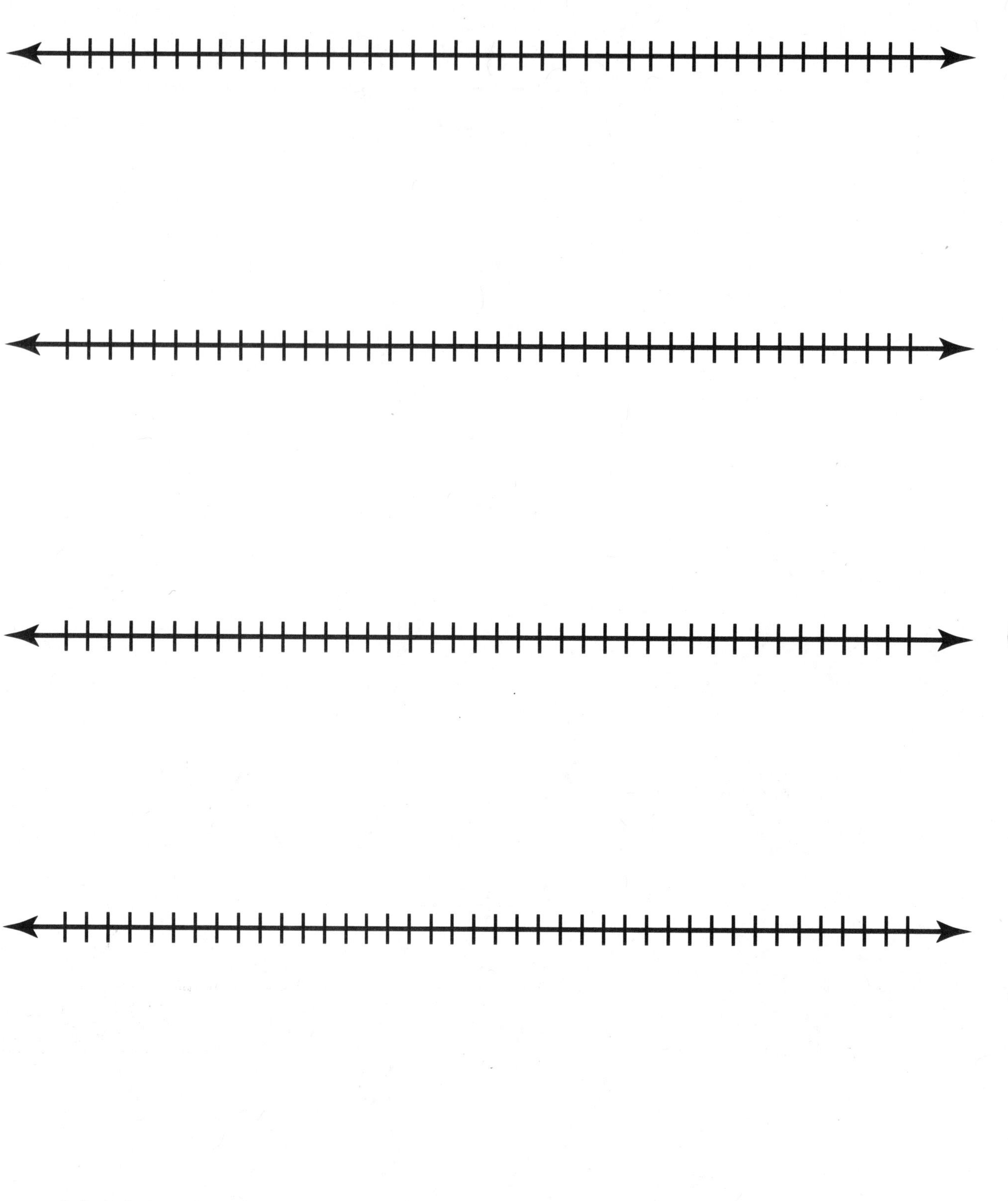

A Chaotic Pattern?

Name ______________________________ Period ____________ Date ______________

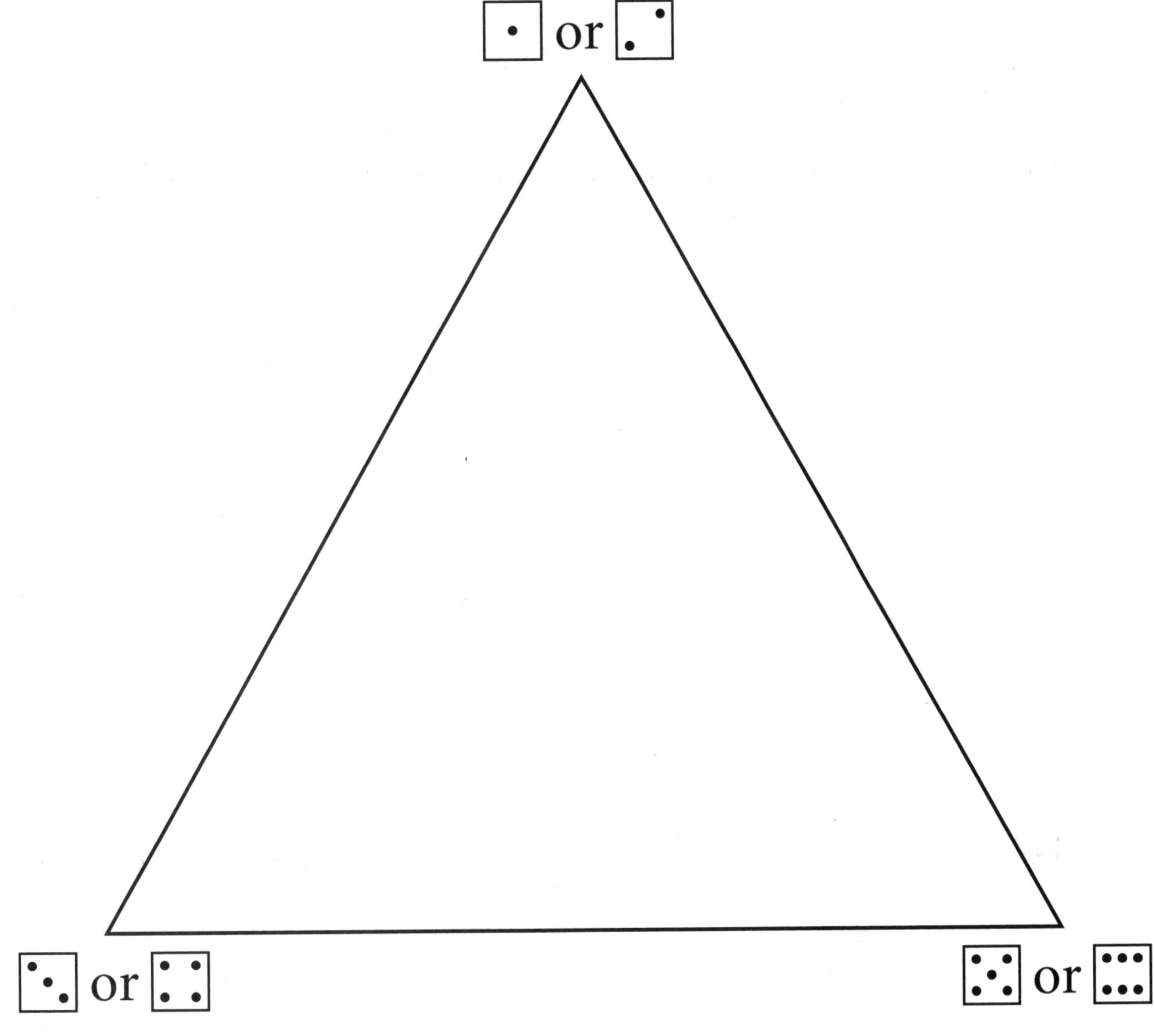

Centimeter Rulers

0 1 2 3 4 5 6 7 8 9 10 11 12 13 14 15
cm

0 1 2 3 4 5 6 7 8 9 10 11 12 13 14 15
cm

0 1 2 3 4 5 6 7 8 9 10 11 12 13 14 15
cm

0 1 2 3 4 5 6 7 8 9 10 11 12 13 14 15
cm

0 1 2 3 4 5 6 7 8 9 10 11 12 13 14 15
cm

Pulse Rate Sample Data

68	76	84	80	76
72	60	68	68	80
68	80	64	64	72
76	72	68	56	88
80	76	68	56	64
60	92	72	84	72

Pennies Sample Data

1977	1980	1982	1984
1986	1986	1988	1989
1991	1991	1993	1994
1994	1996	1997	1997
1998	1998	1998	1999
1999	2001	2002	2003
2005	2006		

Mean

The mean is the sum of the data values divided by the number of data items. The result is often called the average.

Median

For an odd number of data items, the median is the middle value when the data values are listed in order. If there is an even number of data items, then the median is the average of the two middle values.

Mode

The mode is the data value that occurs most often. Data sets can have two modes (bimodal) or more. Some data sets have no mode.

Dot Plot for Pennies

Name ______________________ Period ____________ Date ______________

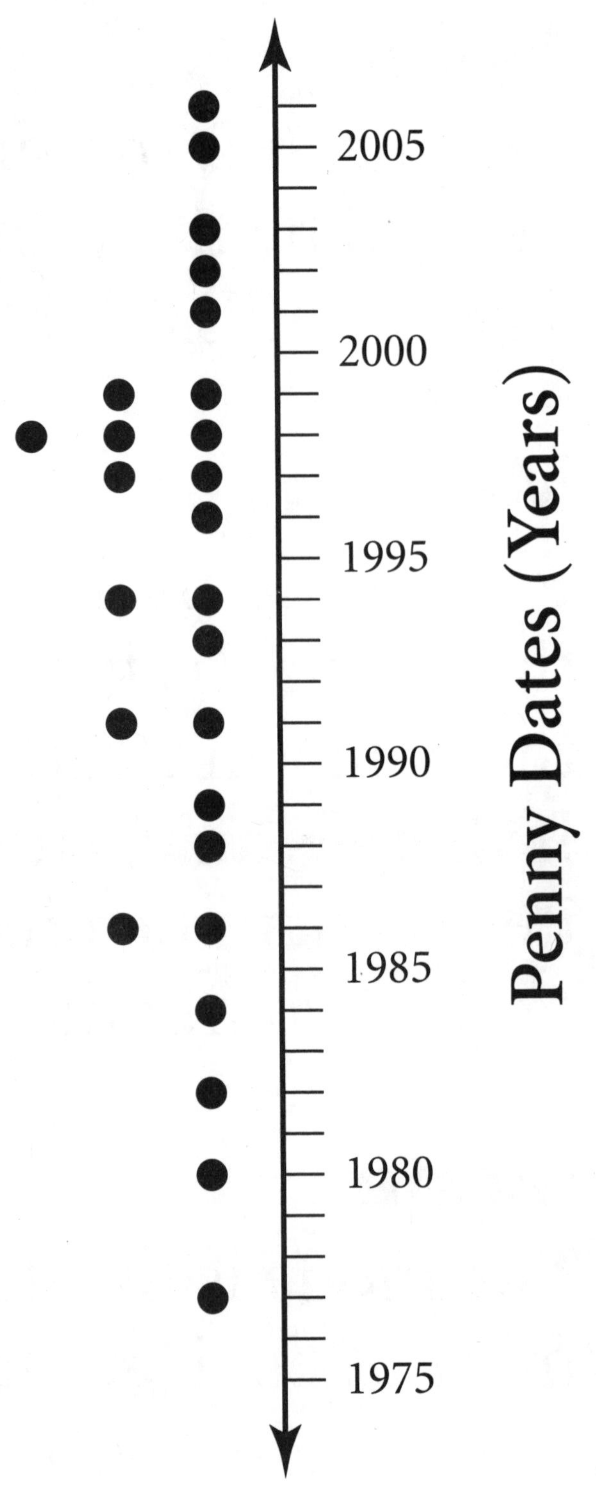

Box Plot for Pennies

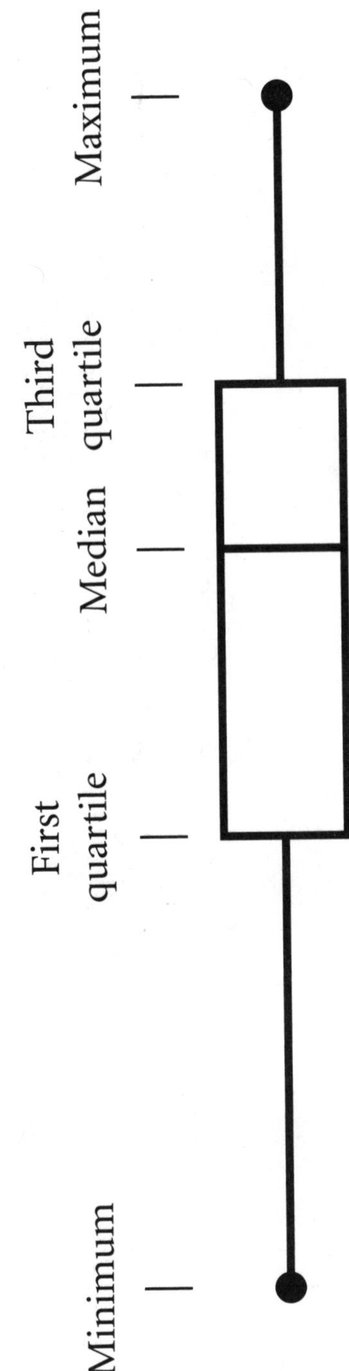

Hand-Span Sample Data

20	22.5	21	19.5
23	20.5	22	19.5
19	21	19	19
21	20.5	21	21.5
20.5	21.5	19.5	20
18	18.5	20	21.5
21	20		

Lab Report

Include the names of all group members, with your name listed first. In Section I, describe both the topic you investigated and the mathematics that you used. In Section II, record the complete set of data. (You can use a computer to print out long data sets from your calculator.) In Section III, provide any graphs of your data that you have made. In Sections IV and V, show your work for all calculations and your conclusions. If you run across anything unusual, make a note of it. It's important to include labels and units throughout the lab report. Be clear and succinct in your descriptions and your conclusions.

Name Your name, Group names **Period** ________ **Date** ________

I. Overview

We measured the hand spans of 15 students in centimeters. We made a data table to summarize our observations, and we found the five-number summary of our data. We created two different histograms and a boxplot to display the data.

II. Data Table

Student #	1	2	3	4	5	6	7	8	9	10	11	12	13	14	15
Hand span (cm)	19	20	20	18	22	19	21.5	18	18.5	20	21	21.5	22	19.5	21

III. Graph(s)

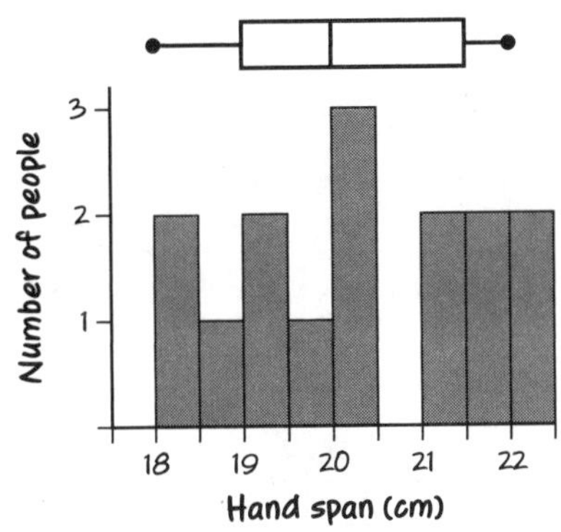

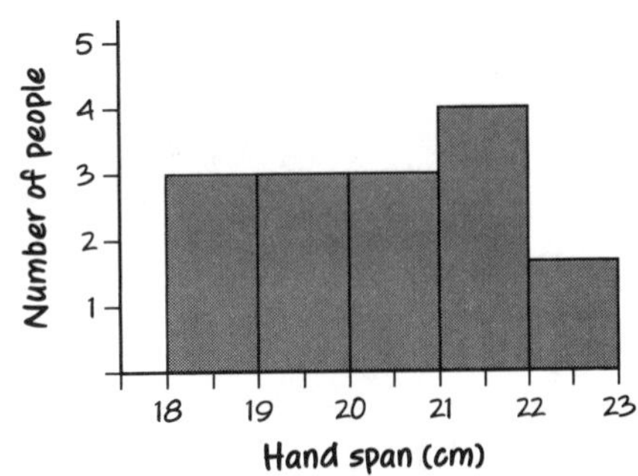

IV. Equations, calculations, and formulas

To find the five-number summary, we listed the data in order from small to large:
18, 18, 18.5, 19, 19, 19.5, 20, 20, 20, 21, 21, 21.5, 21.5, 22, 22.

minimum: 18, Q1: 19, median: 20, Q3: 21.5, maximum: 22.

The mean is 20.7 (we added all the numbers and divided by 15).

The mode is 20, because that is the most common hand-span measure in the data.

V. Conclusions

We found that the box plot clearly shows the five-number summary of the data. The histogram with a bin width of 0.5 made it easy to see the mode and to see that no students had a hand span of 20.5. The bin width of 0.5 was better for this data set because the histogram with a bin width of 1 did not show the missing value of 20.5. The mean, median, and mode are all pretty similar for our data set. Because we only interviewed 15 people, the shapes of our histograms do not reveal much information.

Coordinate Plane

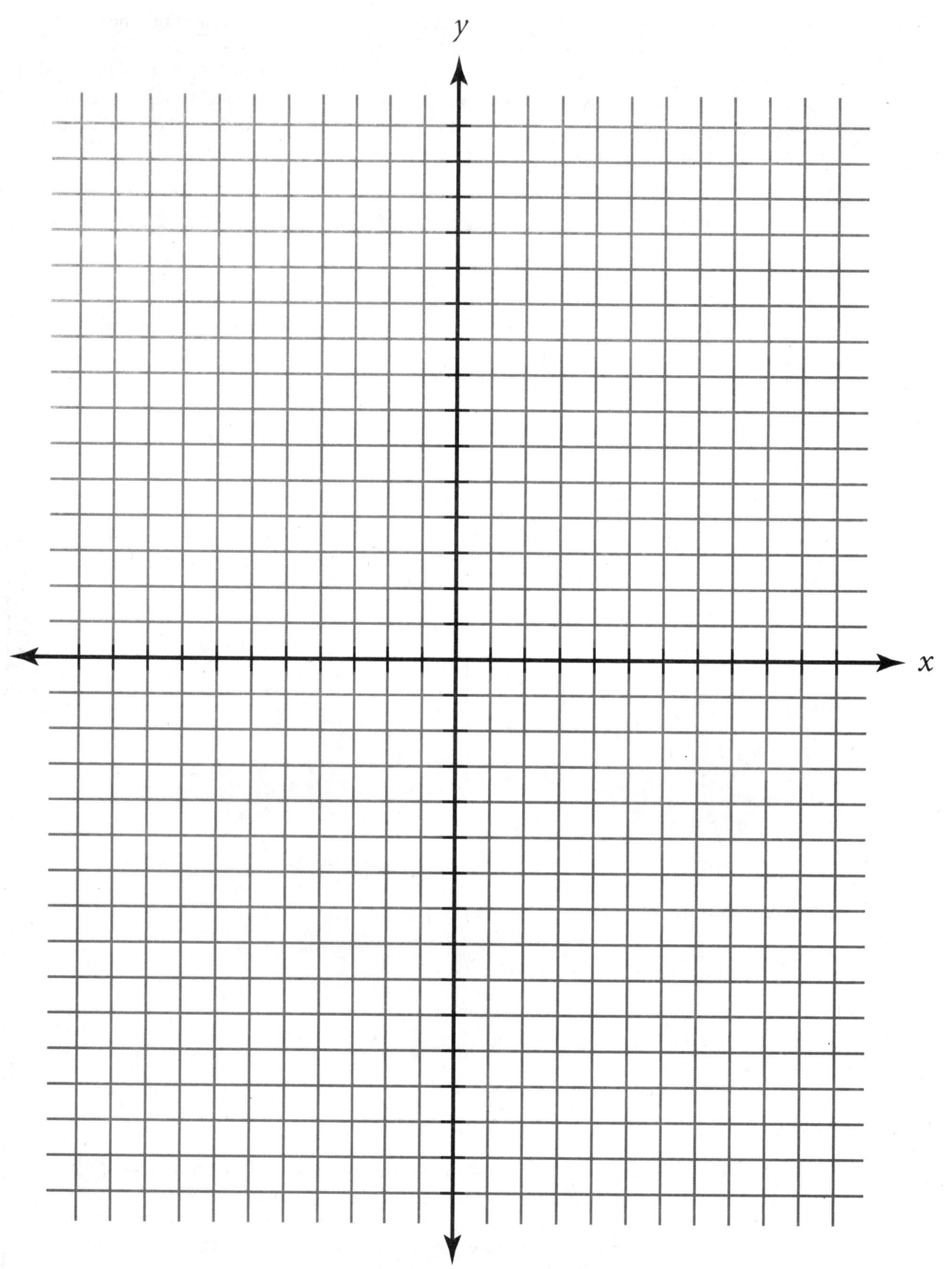

Distance from a Motion Sensor

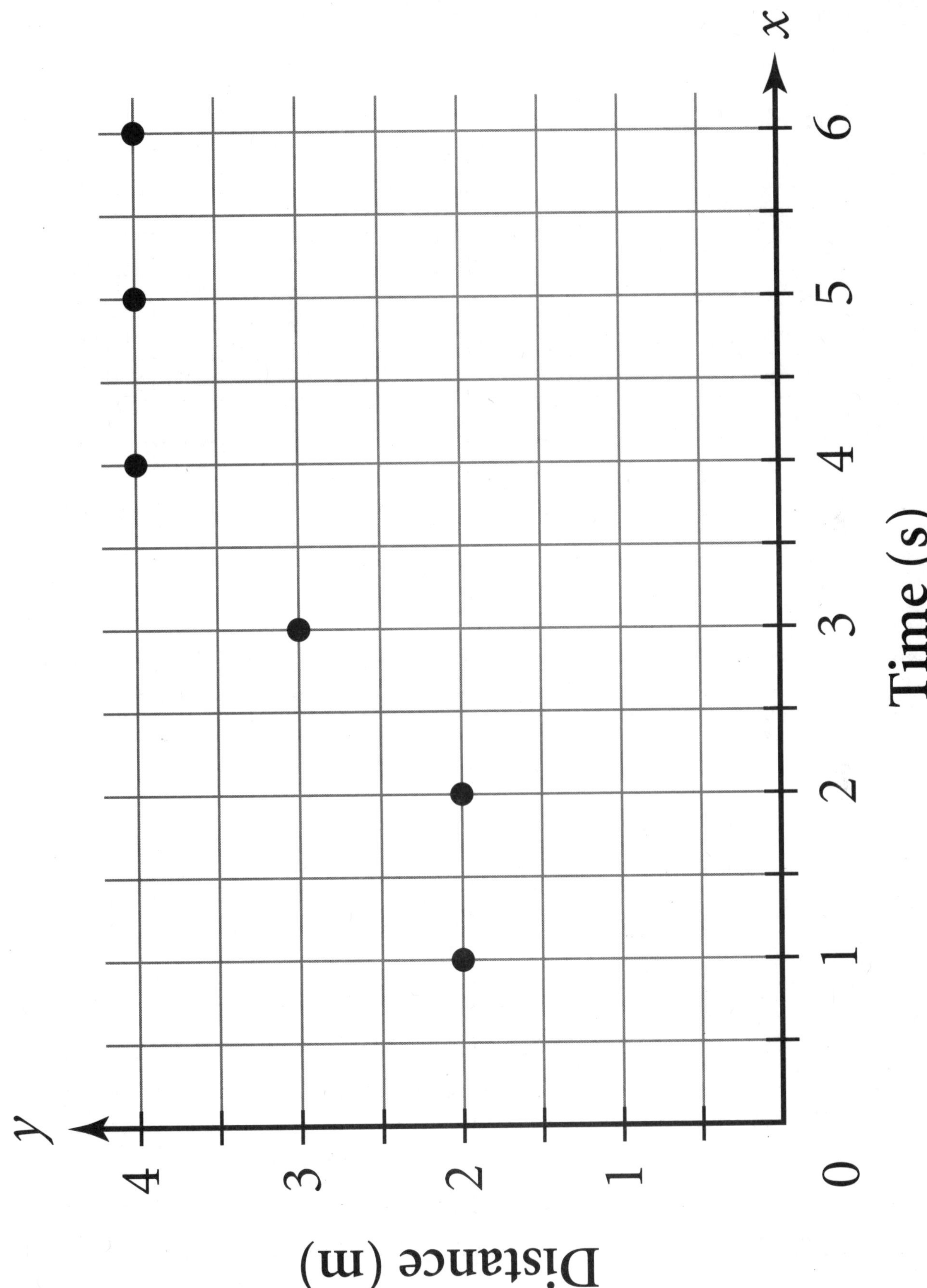

Estimation Investigation: Age at Death

Name ______________________ Period __________ Date ______________

Name	Estimated age (yr)	Actual age (yr)	
John Lennon			40
Richard Nixon			81
Princess Diana			36
Dr. Benjamin Spock			94
Martin Luther King, Jr.			39
Marilyn Monroe			36
Frank Sinatra			82
James Michener			90
Linda McCartney			56
Ryan White			18
Lou Gehrig			37
Gilda Radner			42
Su Shueh-lin			104
Florence Griffith Joyner			38
James Dean			24
Agnes Gonxha Bojaxhiu (Mother Teresa)			87
Mourning Dove			48
César Chávez			66
El Hajj Malik al-Shabazz (Malcolm X)			39
Ella Maria Gonzales Alvarez			93
Akira Kurosawa			88
Nizar Qabbani			75
Michael Hedges			43
Marie-Louise van Franz			83
Tom Bradley			80
Wilma Randolph			54

Estimation Investigation: Average Gestation Period

Name ______________________ Period __________ Date ______________

Species	Estimated gestation (days)	Actual gestation (days)	
Asian elephant			645
Lion			100
Domestic cat			63
Meadow mouse			21
Leopard			98
Guinea pig			68
Cow			284
Polar bear			240
Domestic rabbit			31
Domestic pig			112
White rhinosaurus			480
Gorilla			258
Human			280
Giraffe			457
Chipmunk			31

(*The World Almanac and Book of Facts 2004*, p. 179)

Estimation Investigation: Maximum Speed

Name ______________________ Period __________ Date ____________

Species	Estimated speed (mi/h over quarter mile)	Actual speed (mi/h)	
Cheetah			70
Lion			50
Reindeer			32
Human			28
Domestic rabbit			35
Chicken			9
Zebra			40
Pig			11
Greyhound			39
Domestic cat			30
Grizzly bear			30
Wild turkey			15
Quarter horse			47.5
Three-toed sloth			0.15
Garden snail			0.03
Gray fox			42
Spider			1.17

(*Natural History* magazine, in *The World Almanac and Book of Facts 2004*, p. 179)

Large-Item Prices

	Pizza Palace	Tony's Pizzeria
Large pizza	\$11.40	\$11.35
Large salad	\$3.35	\$3.90
Large drink	\$2.15	\$2.10

Fish in the Lake Sample Data

Sample number	Number of tagged fish	Total number of fish	Ratio of tagged fish to total fish
1	3	60	$\frac{3}{60}$, or $\frac{1}{20}$
2	6	67	$\frac{6}{67}$
3	3	73	$\frac{3}{73}$
4	4	66	$\frac{4}{66}$, or $\frac{2}{33}$
5	4	88	$\frac{4}{88}$, or $\frac{1}{22}$
6	2	72	$\frac{2}{72}$, or $\frac{1}{36}$

Ship Canals

Canal	Length (miles)	Length (kilometers)
Albert (Belgium)	80	129
Alphonse XIII (Spain)	53	85
Houston (Texas)	50	81
Kiel (Germany)	62	99
Main-Danube (Germany)	106	171
Moscow-Volga (Russia)	80	129
Panama (Panama)	51	82
St. Lawrence Seaway (Canada/United States)	189	304
Suez (Egypt)	101	
Trollhätte (Sweden)		87

(*The Top 10 of Everything 1998*, p. 57)

Seesaw Nickels

Name ______________________________ Period __________ Date ______________

If a grown man and a small child sit on opposite ends of a seesaw, what happens? Would changing or moving the weight on one end of the seesaw affect the balance? You'll find out as you do the experiment in this investigation. You will need a pencil, a 12-inch ruler, nine nickels, and tape.

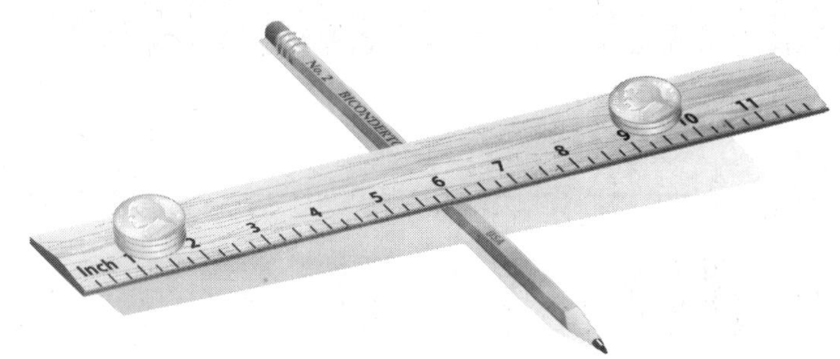

Step 1 On a flat desk or table, try to balance the ruler across a pencil near the ruler's 6-inch mark.

Step 2 Stack two nickels on the ruler so that they're centered 3 inches to the right of the pencil. You may need to tape them in place.

Step 3 Place one nickel on the left side of the ruler so that it balances the two right-side nickels. Be sure that the ruler stays centered over the pencil. How far from the pencil is this one nickel centered?

Step 4 Repeat Step 3 for two, three, four, and six nickels on the left side of the ruler. Measure to the nearest $\frac{1}{2}$ inch. Copy and complete this table.

Left side		Right side	
Number of nickels	**Distance from pencil**	**Number of nickels**	**Distance from pencil**
1		2	3
2		2	3
3		2	3
4		2	3
6		2	3

Step 5 As you increase the number of nickels on the left side, how does the distance from the balance point change? What relationships do you notice?

Step 6 Make a new table and repeat the investigation with three nickels stacked 3 inches to the right of center. Does the same relationship seem to hold true?

Step 7 Review the data in your tables. How does the number of nickels on the left and their distance from the pencil compare to the number of nickels on the right and their distance from the pencil? In each of your tables, do quantities remain constant? Write a sentence using the words *left nickels, right nickels, left distance,* and *right distance* to explain the relationship between the quantities in this investigation. Define variables and rewrite your sentence as an equation.

Step 8 Explain why you think this relationship between the number of nickels on the left side and the distance from the pencil is an *inverse* relationship.

Direct Variation

An equation of the form $y = kx$ is a **direct variation.** The quantities represented by x and y are **directly proportional,** and k is the **constant of variation.**

Inverse Variation

An equation of the form $y = \frac{k}{x}$ is an **inverse variation.** Quantities represented by x and y are **inversely proportional,** and k is the **constant of variation.**

1. Evaluate expressions within parentheses or other grouping symbols.
2. Evaluate all powers.
3. Multiply and divide from left to right.
4. Add and subtract from left to right.

Cross-Number Puzzle

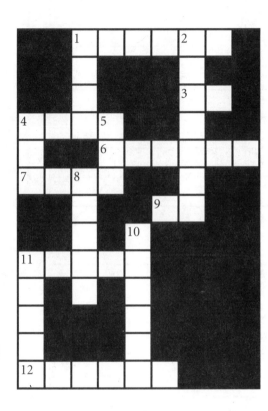

Name ______________________ Period ________ Date __________

Across

1. $\frac{2}{3}$ of 159,327

3. $\dfrac{-1 + 17^2}{4 + 2^2}$

4. $4835 - 541 + 1284$

6. $\dfrac{3 + 140}{3 \cdot 14}$ (fraction form)

7. $8075 - 3(42)$

9. $\sqrt{6^2 + 8^2}$

11. $\dfrac{740}{18.4 - 2.1 \cdot 9}$

12. 57^3

Down

1. $9(-7 + 180)$

2. $\left(\frac{9}{2}\right)\left(\frac{17}{5} + \frac{25}{4}\right)$ (fraction form)

4. $3 - 3(12 - 200)$

5. $9 \cdot 10^2 - 9^2$

8. $15 + 47(922)$

10. $25.9058 \cdot 20/4 - 89$ (decimal form)

11. $1284 - \dfrac{877}{0.2}$

Undoing Operations

Equation:	=	
Description	**Undo**	**Result**
		$x =$

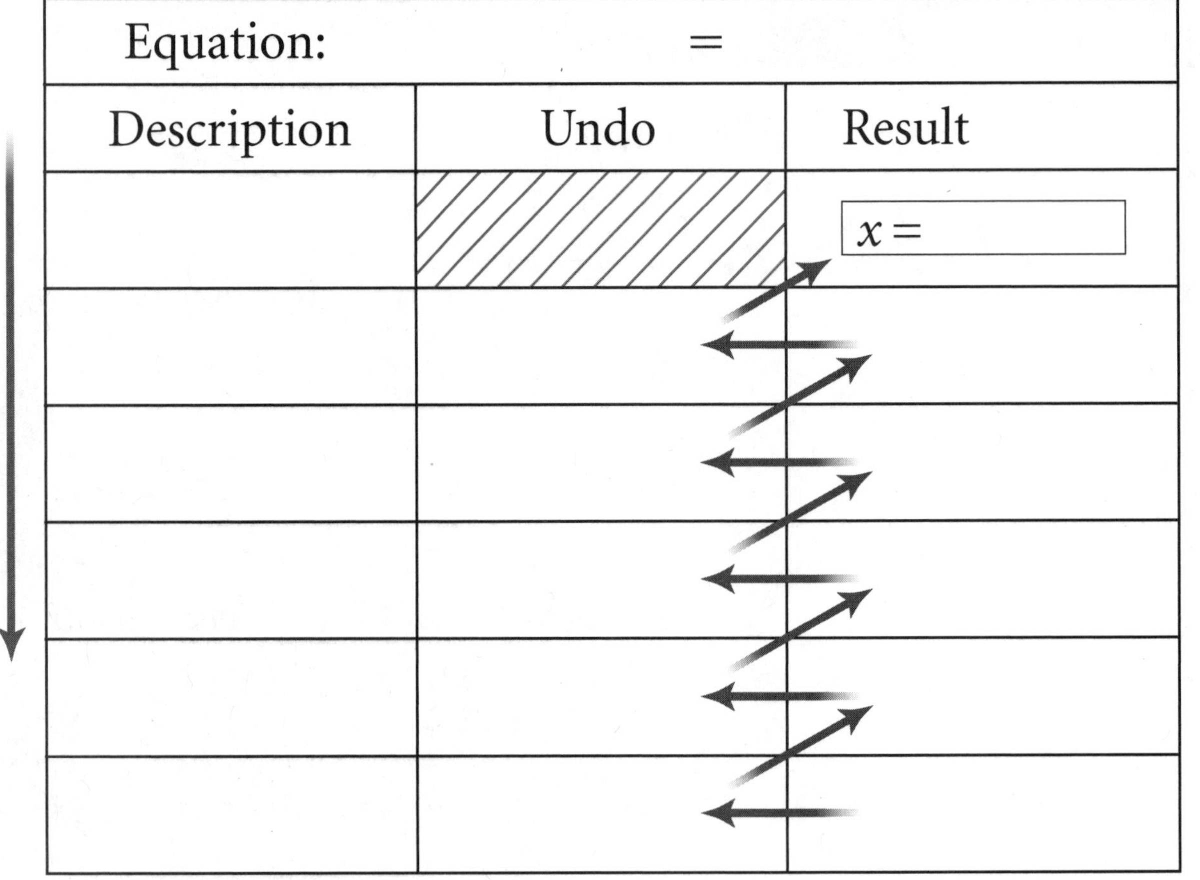

Equation:	=	
Description	**Undo**	**Result**
		$x =$

Elevator Table

Floor number	Height (ft)
0 (basement)	−4
1	9
2	22
3	35
4	48
. . .	. . .

On the Road Again Table

Name ______________________________ Period ____________ Date ______________

Highway Distance from Flint

Time (min)	Minivan (mi)	Sports car (mi)	Pickup (mi)
0			
1			
2			
5			
10			
20			

On the Road Again Grid

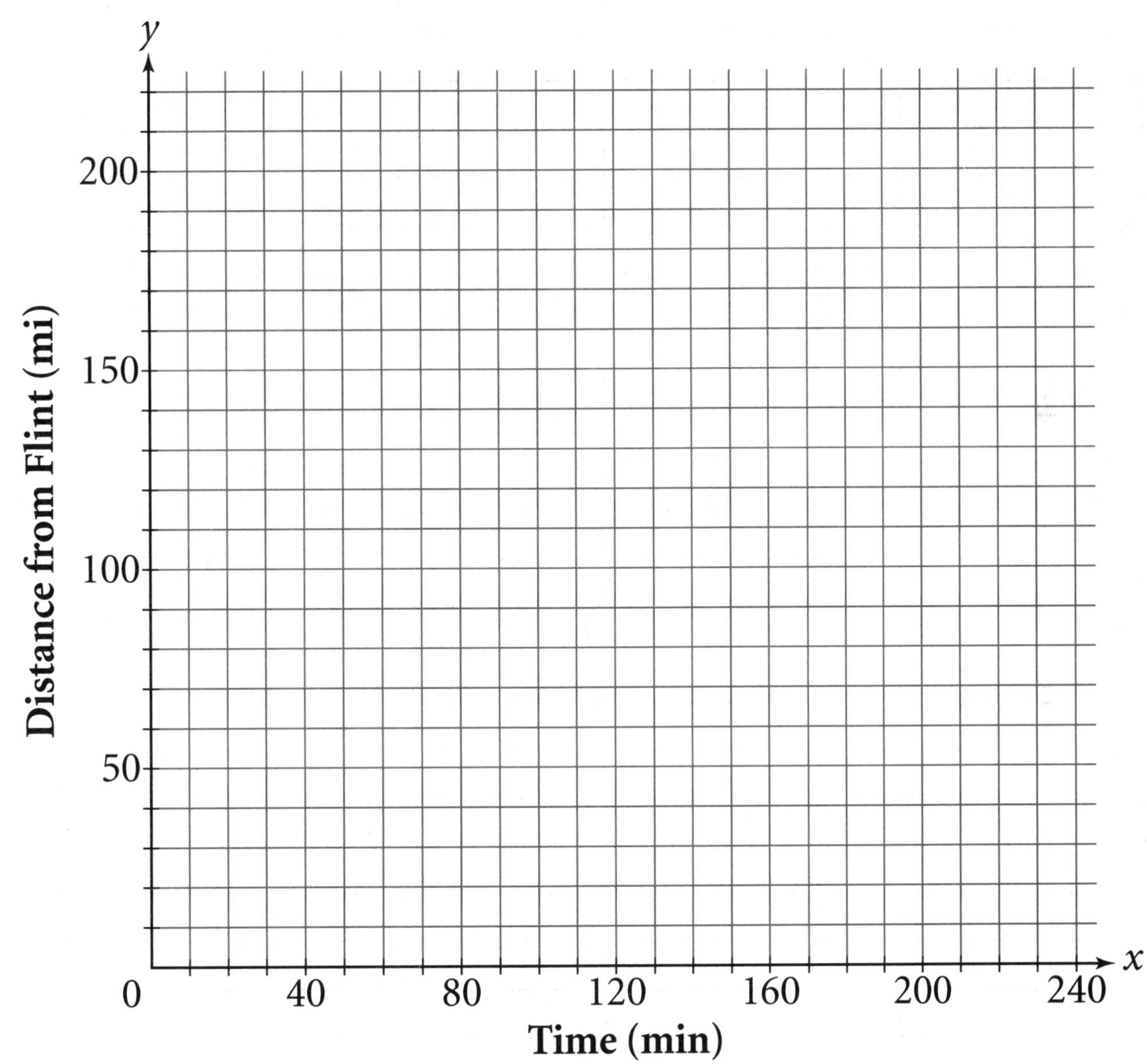

On the Road Again Graph

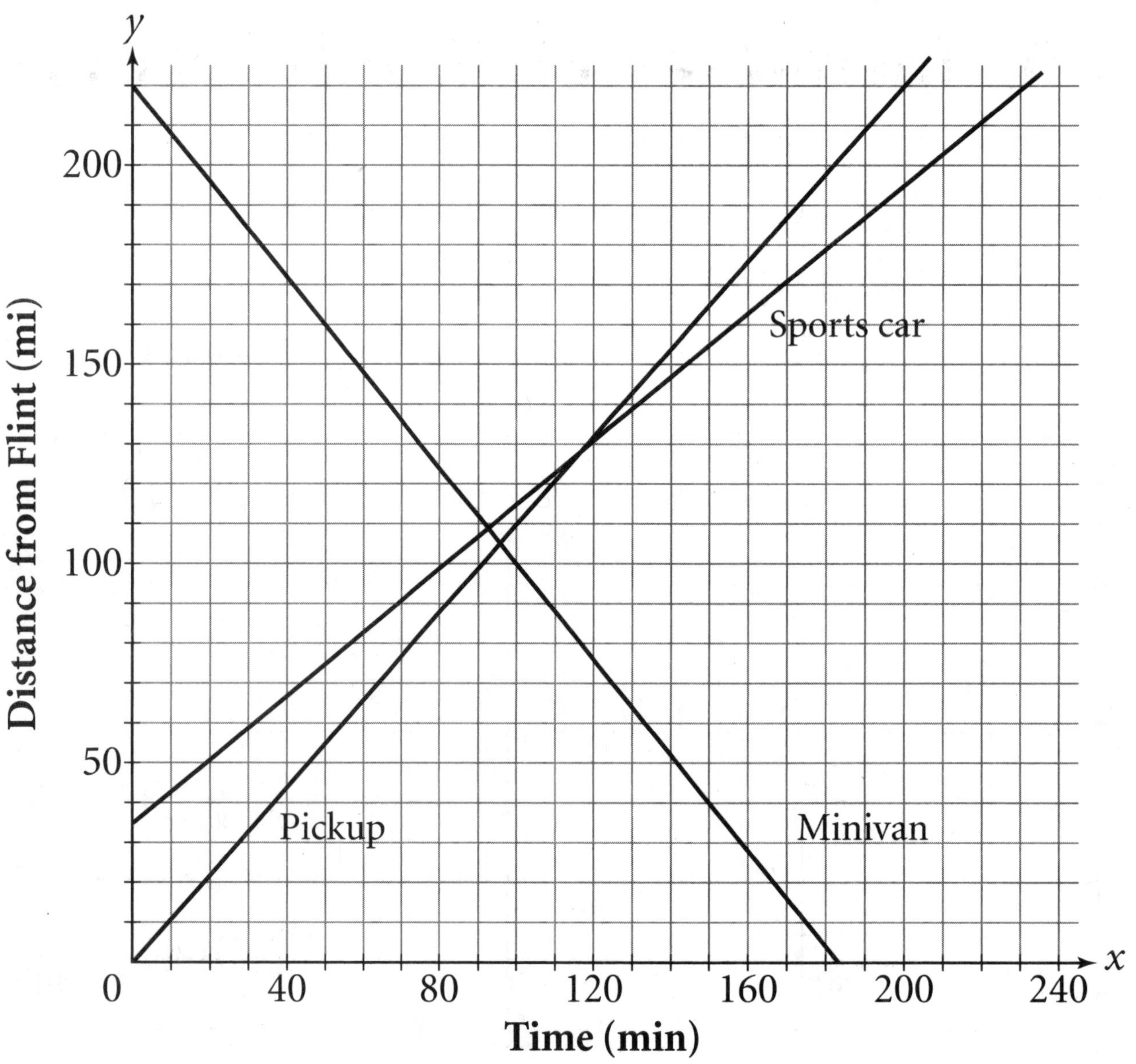

Wind Chill for Winds of 20 Miles Per Hour

Temperature (°F)	Wind chill (°F)
−5	−28.540
0	−21.980
1	−20.668
2	−19.356
5	−15.420
15	−2.300
35	23.940

Pan Balance

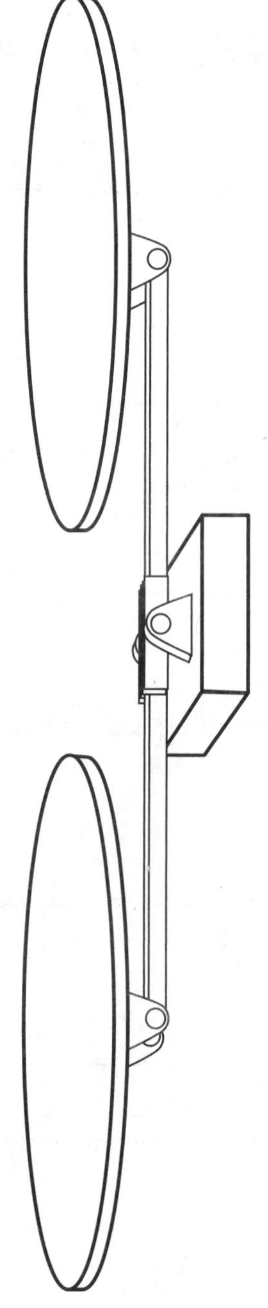

The Four Slope Types

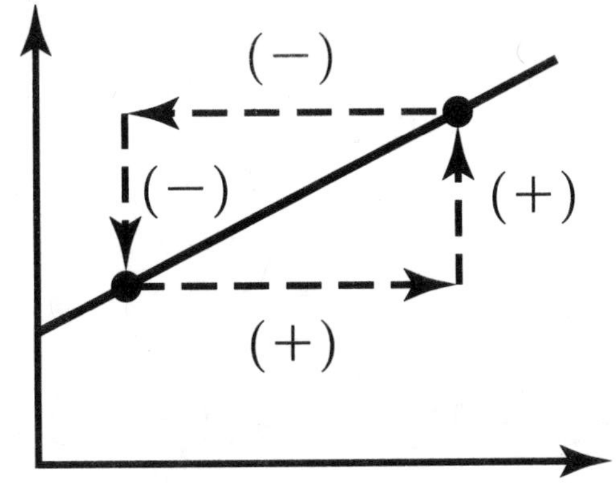

The change in y and the change in x are both positive or both negative. The ratio $\frac{\textit{change in } y}{\textit{change in } x}$ will be positive, so the slope is positive.

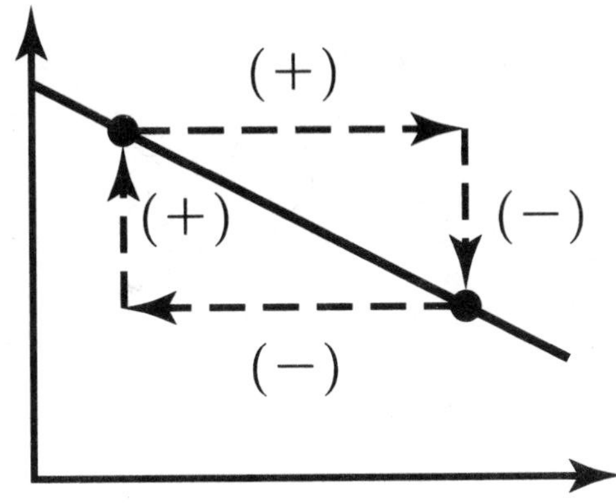

The change in y is positive but the change in x is negative. Or the change in y is negative but the change in x is positive. The ratio $\frac{\textit{change in } y}{\textit{change in } x}$ will be negative, so the slope is negative.

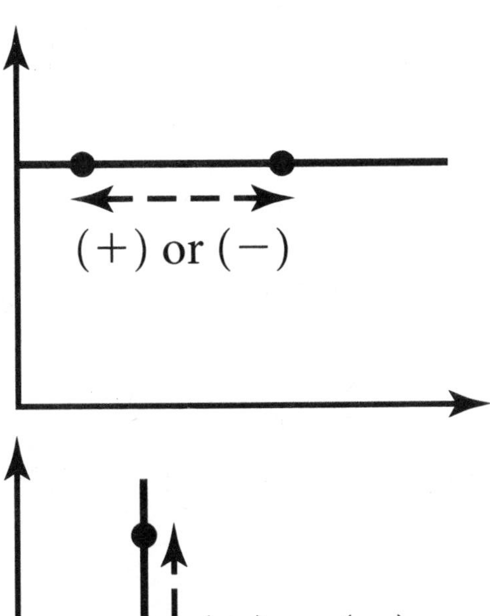

The change in y is zero and the change in x is positive or negative. The ratio becomes $\frac{0}{\textit{change in } x}$, so the slope is 0.

The change in y is positive or negative and the change in x is zero. The ratio becomes $\frac{\textit{change in } y}{0}$, and the slope is undefined.

Properties of Numbers

For any values of *a*, *b*, and *c*, these properties are true:

Distributive Property

$a(b + c) = a(b) + a(c)$ Example: $6(-2 + 3) = 6(-2) + 6(3)$

Commutative Property of Addition

$a + b = b + a$ Example: $3 + 4 = 4 + 3$

Commutative Property of Multiplication

$ab = ba$ Example: $\frac{1}{2} \cdot \frac{3}{4} = \frac{3}{4} \cdot \frac{1}{2}$

Associative Property of Addition

$a + (b + c) = (a + b) + c$ Example: $2 + (1.5 + 3) = (2 + 1.5) + 3$

Associative Property of Multiplication

$a(bc) = (ab)c$ Example: $4\left(\frac{1}{3} \cdot 6.3\right) = \left(4 \cdot \frac{1}{3}\right)6.3$

Given $a = b$, for any number c,

Addition Property of Equality

$a + c = b + c$

Subtraction Property of Equality

$a - c = b - c$

Multiplication Property of Equality

$ac = bc$

Division Property of Equality

$\frac{a}{c} = \frac{b}{c} \quad (c \neq 0)$

Rope Sample Data

Type 1 Rope	
Knots	Length (cm)
0	89.9
1	85.6
2	81.2
3	77.7
4	72.1
5	68.9
6	63.6

Type 2 Rope	
Knots	Length (cm)
0	93.9
1	89.9
2	85.8
3	81.6
4	77.2
5	72.4
6	67.4

Type 3 Rope	
Knots	Length (cm)
0	100
1	94
2	88
3	81.3
4	75.7
5	69.9
6	63.5

Type 4 Rope	
Knots	Length (cm)
0	100
1	89.7
2	78.7
3	68.6
4	57.4
5	47.8
6	38.1

Type 5 Rope	
Knots	Length (cm)
0	97.8
1	83.2
2	71.0
3	57.1
4	43.8
5	31.0
6	—

- Multiply (or divide) all numbers in a row by a nonzero number.
- Add all numbers in a row to corresponding numbers in another row.
- Add a multiple of the numbers in one row to the corresponding numbers in another row.
- Exchange two rows.

Toe the Line

Operation	Walker A's position	Inequality symbol	Walker B's position
Starting number	2		4
Add 2			
Subtract 3			
Add -2			
Subtract -4			
Multiply by 2			
Subtract 7			
Multiply by -3			
Add 5			
Divide by -4			
Subtract 2			
Multiply by -1			

Number Line

Name ______________________ Period __________ Date ______________

Graphing Inequalities Grids

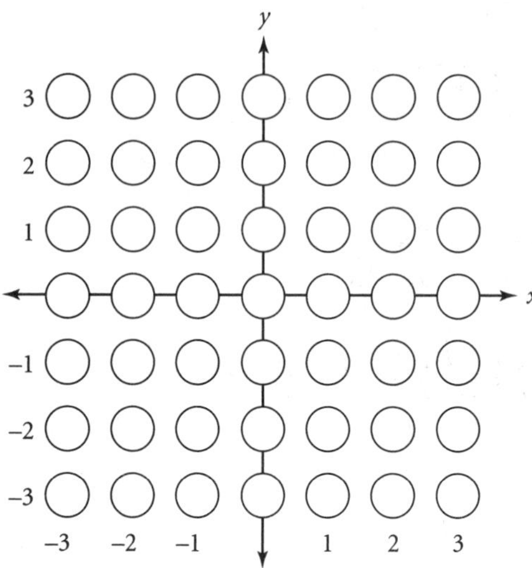

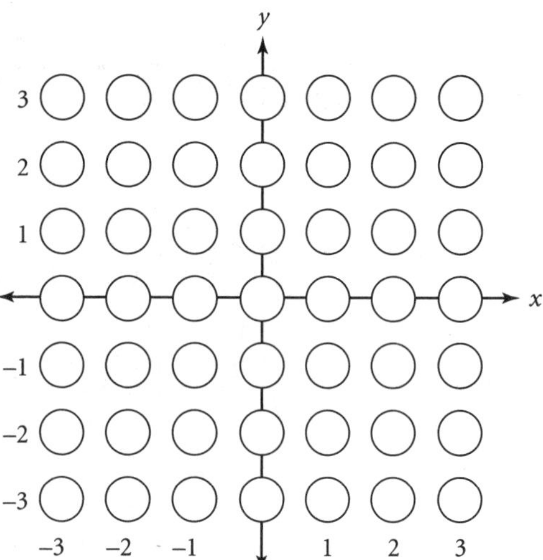

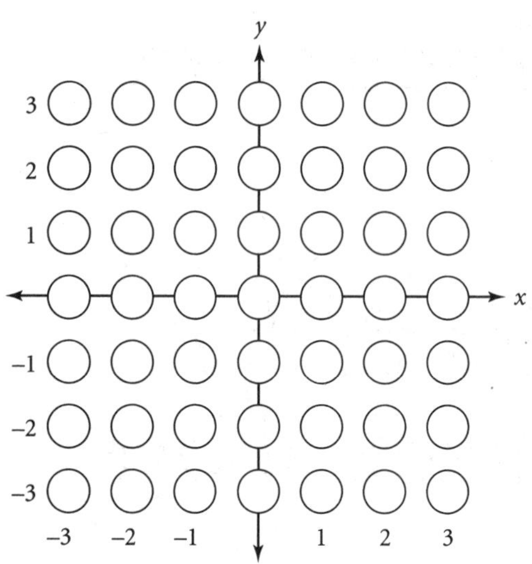

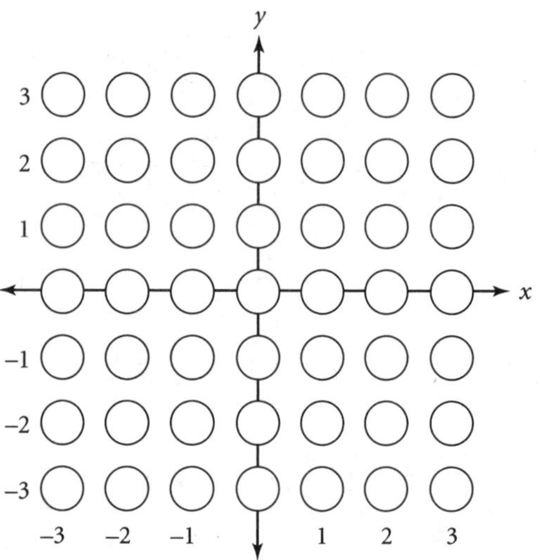

Draw a broken or dashed line on the boundary for inequalities with $>$ or $<$.

Draw a solid line on the boundary for inequalities with $\geq$ or $\leq$.

To graph inequalities in the form $y <$ or $y \leq$, shade below the boundary line.

To graph inequalities in the form $y >$ or $y \geq$, shade above the boundary line.

Cereal Sales and Profit

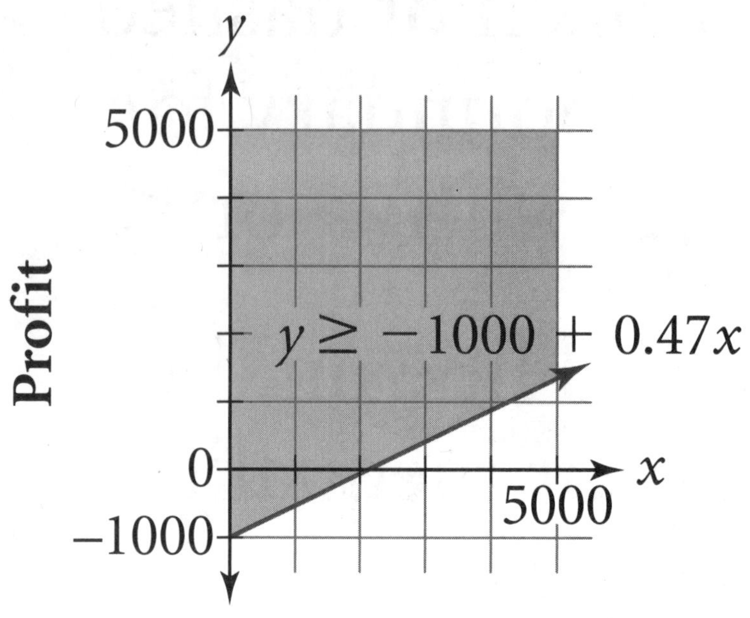

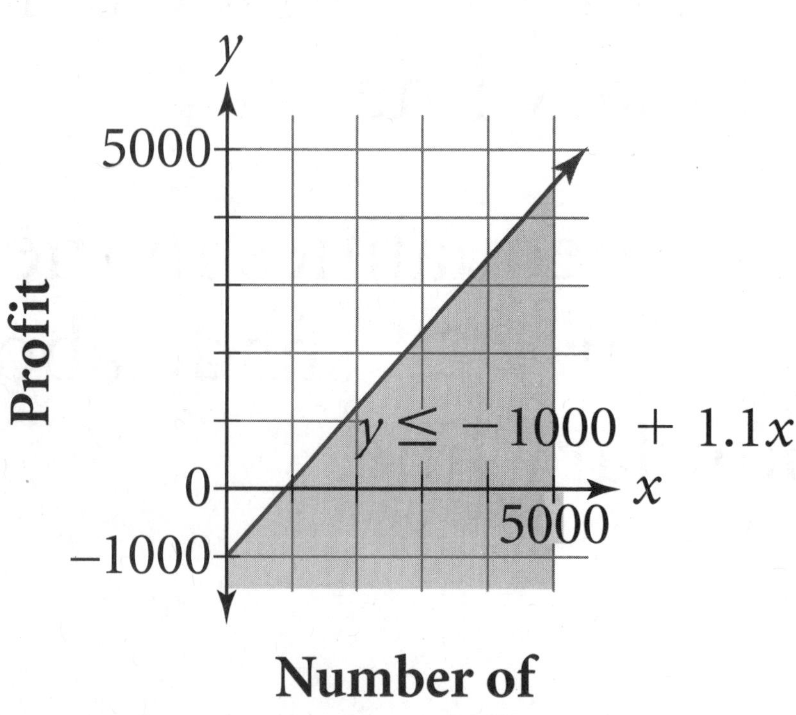

Growth of the Koch Curve

Name ______________________ Period __________ Date ______________

Stage 0

Stage 1

Stage 2

Stage 3

Koch Curve with Sketchpad

Name ______________________________ Period __________ Date ______________

1. Open a new Sketchpad document. Choose **Preferences** from the Edit menu. On the Units panel, set the units for Distance to **cm.** On the Text panel, check Show Labels Automatically For All New Points.
2. Click on the **Segment** tool. Draw a horizontal segment (hold the shift key while drawing to keep it horizontal). Choose **Length** from the Measure menu.
3. Click on the **Selection Arrow.** Move one endpoint of the segment until the length is 27 cm, keeping the segment horizontal.
4. Select the first endpoint (A) and choose **Mark Center** from the Transform menu. Select the second endpoint (B), choose **Dilate** from the Transform menu, and dilate point B by a ratio of 1 to 3.
5. Choose the **Label** tool. Double-click the label of the new point (B') and relabel it C.
6. Dilate point B again, this time by a ratio of 2 to 3. Label the new point D.
7. Mark point C as a center. Select point D and choose **Rotate** from the Transform menu. Rotate point D by a fixed angle of 60°. Label the new point E.
8. You are almost there! Use the **Segment** tool to connect the points in this order: A, C, E, D, B. Then, use the **Selection** tool to click on the original segment AB. Choose **Hide Segment** from the Display menu.

9. Measure each segment to check that they are the same length. Then, choose **Calculate** from the Measure menu and find the sum of all the segments. Click on a measure to add it to the calculation.
10. Select all the points and segments. From the Custom Tools menu, choose **Create New Tool** and name it Koch.
11. Click on white space to deselect everything. Click the **Segment** tool and choose **Select All Segments** from the Edit menu, then choose **Hide Segments** from the Display menu.
12. Now you will use the **Koch** tool to create Stage 2. Choose the **Koch** tool from the Custom Tools menu, then select each pair of points in order: A and C, C and E, E and D, and D and B. Measure several of the segments to find the lengths.
13. Repeat Steps 11 and 12 to create Stage 3 and Stage 4. *Note:* To hide the point labels, select the **Point** tool, and choose **Select All Points** from the Edit menu. Then choose **Hide Labels** from the Display menu.

Multiplication Property of Exponents

For any values of b, m, and n,

$$b^m \cdot b^n = b^{m+n}$$

Power Properties of Exponents

For any values a, b, m, and n,

$$(b^m)^n = b^{mn}$$

$$(ab)^n = a^n b^n$$

Division Property of Exponents

For any nonzero value of b and any values of m and n,

$$\frac{b^n}{b^m} = b^{n-m}$$

Negative Exponents and Exponents of Zero

For any nonzero value of b and for any value of n,

$$b^{-n} = \frac{1}{b^n} \quad \text{or} \quad \frac{1}{b^{-n}} = b^n$$

$$b^0 = 1$$

100 Grid

Name ______________________ Period __________ Date __________

0	1	2	3	4	5	6	7	8	9
10	11	12	13	14	15	16	17	18	19
20	21	22	23	24	25	26	27	28	29
30	31	32	33	34	35	36	37	38	39
40	41	42	43	44	45	46	47	48	49
50	51	52	53	54	55	56	57	58	59
60	61	62	63	64	65	66	67	68	69
70	71	72	73	74	75	76	77	78	79
80	81	82	83	84	85	86	87	88	89
90	91	92	93	94	95	96	97	98	99

Protractors

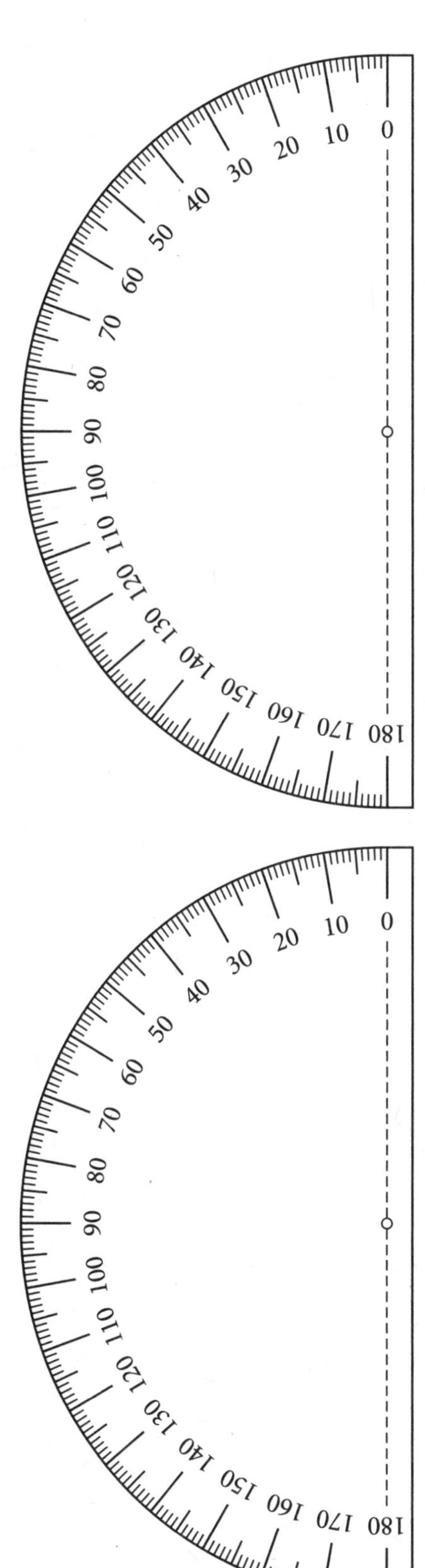

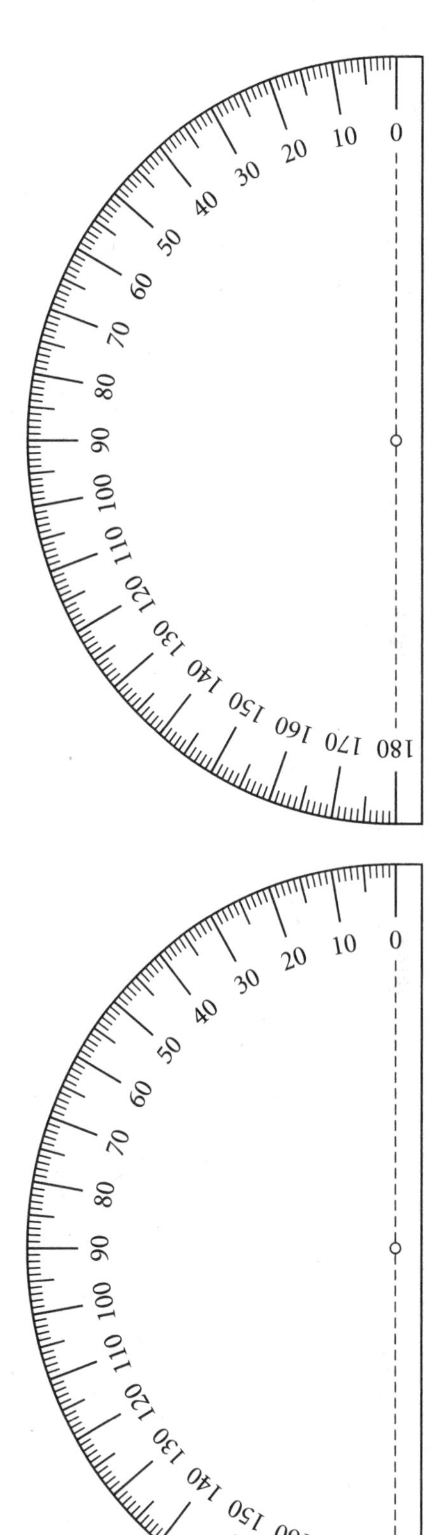

Radioactive Decay Sample Data

Years elapsed	Atoms remaining
0	201
1	147
2	120
3	94
4	71
5	52
6	42
7	32
8	28
9	22
10	18
11	15
12	12
13	10
14	9

Moore's Law Sample Data

Intel Processors

Processor (year released)	Years since 1971	Number of transistors
4004 (1971)	0	2,300
8080 (1974)	3	6,000
8086 (1978)	7	29,000
80286 (1982)	11	134,000
80386 DX (1985)	14	275,000
80486 DX (1989)	18	1,200,000
Pentium (1993)	22	3,100,000
Pentium Pro (1995)	24	5,500,000
Pentium II (1997)	26	7,500,000
Pentium III (2000)	29	28,000,000

(*www.intel.com*)

Bounce Sample Data

Bounce number	Maximum rebound height (m)
0	1.00
1	0.75
2	0.45
3	0.28
4	0.19
5	0.13
6	0.09

Pendulum Sample Data

Swing number	Maximum distance from center (m)
0	0.50
1	0.48
2	0.45
3	0.45
4	0.43
5	0.40
6	0.40
7	0.38
8	0.38
9	0.35
10	0.33
11	0.33
12	0.30
13	0.30
14	0.28
15	0.28

Swing number	Maximum distance from center (m)
16	0.25
17	0.25
18	0.25
19	0.23
20	0.23
21	0.23
22	0.20
23	0.20
24	0.18
25	0.18
26	0.18
27	0.15
28	0.15
29	0.15
30	0.15

Coding Grid

Name ______________________________ Period ____________ Date ________________

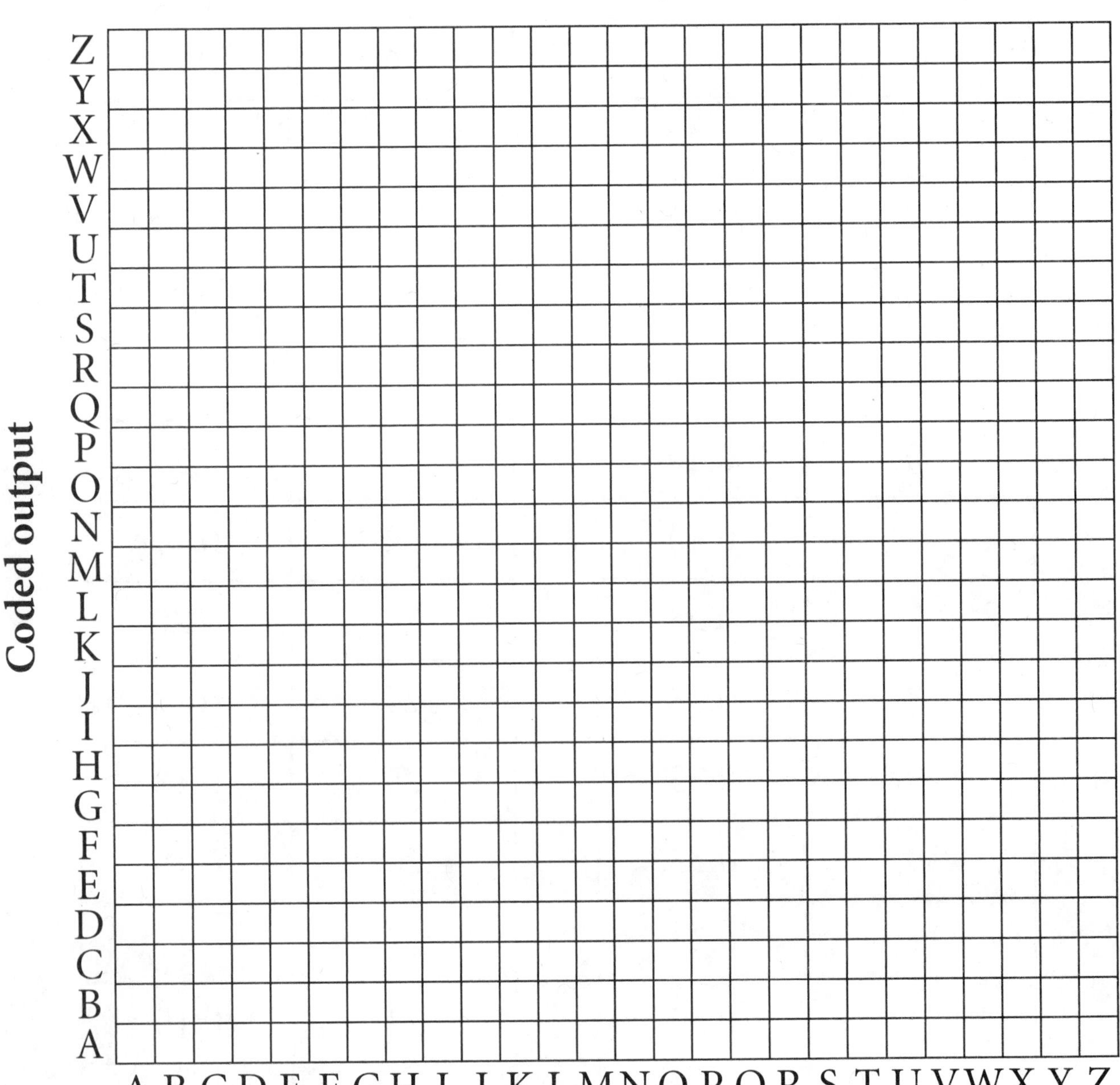

TFDSFU DPEFT

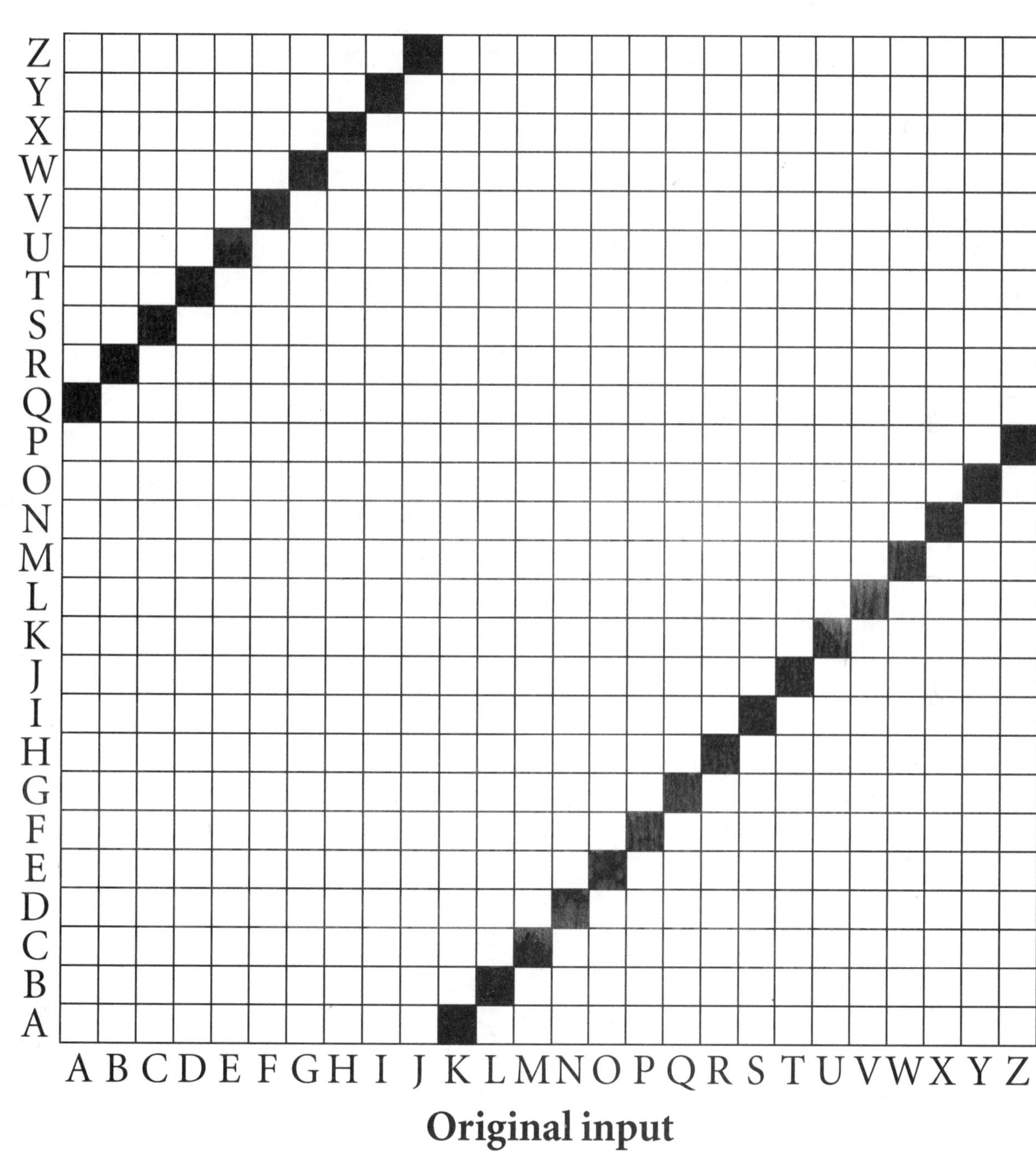

Function or Not?

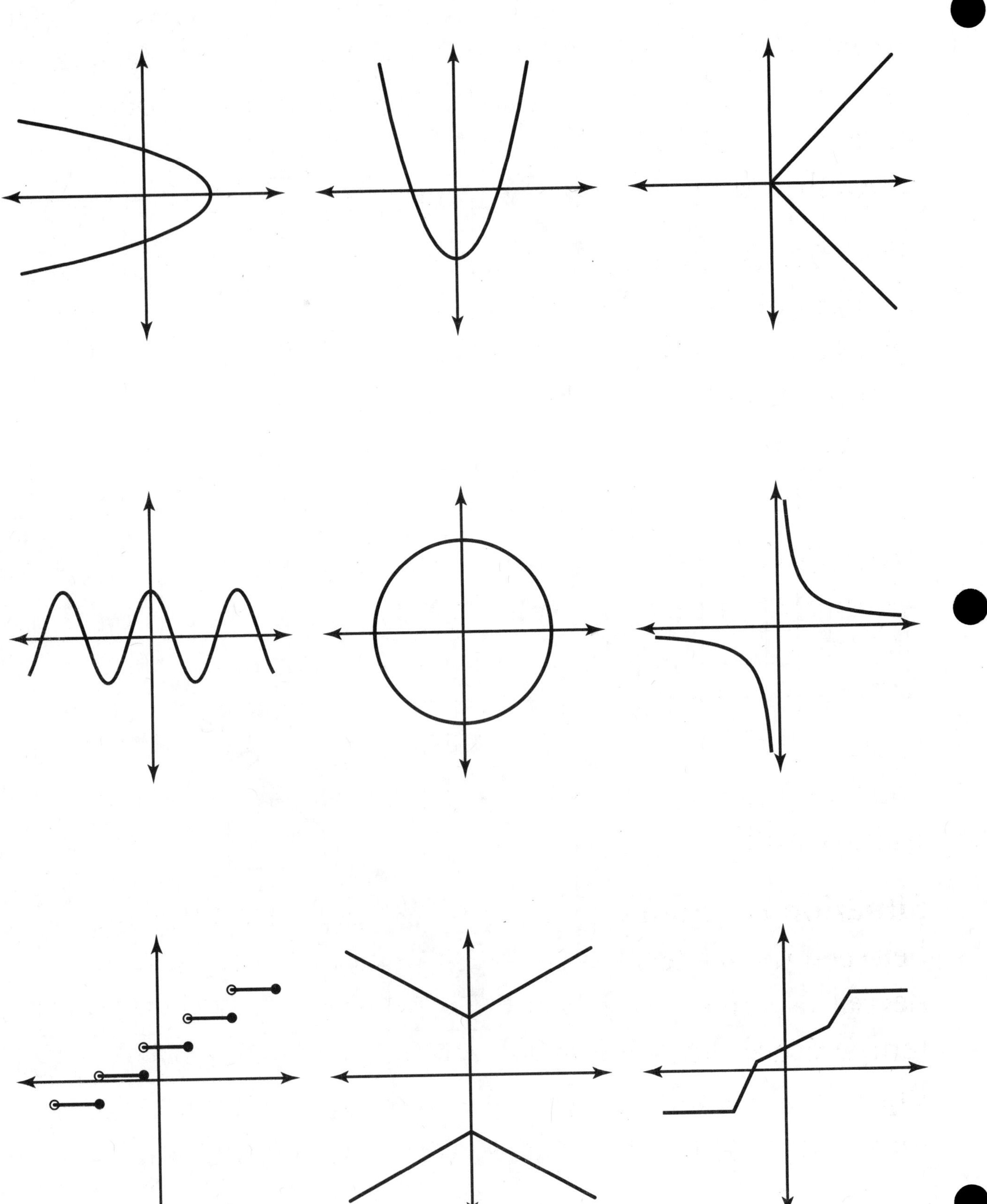

Situation A During the first few years, the number of deer on the island increased by a steady percentage. As food became less plentiful, the growth rate started slowing down. Now, the number of births and deaths is about the same.

Situation B In the Northern Hemisphere the amount of daylight increases slowly from January through February, faster until mid-May, and then slowly until the maximum in June. Then it decreases slowly through July, faster from August until mid-November, and then slowly until the year's end.

Situation C If you have a fixed amount of fencing, the width of your rectangular garden determines its area. If the width is very short, the garden won't have much area. As the width increases, the area also increases. The area increases more slowly until it reaches a maximum. As the width continues to increase, the area becomes smaller more quickly until it is zero.

Situation D Your cup of tea is very hot. The difference between the tea temperature and the room temperature decreases quickly at first as the tea starts to cool to room temperature. But when the two temperatures are close together, the cooling rate slows down. It actually takes a long time for the tea to finally reach room temperature.

Water Depth

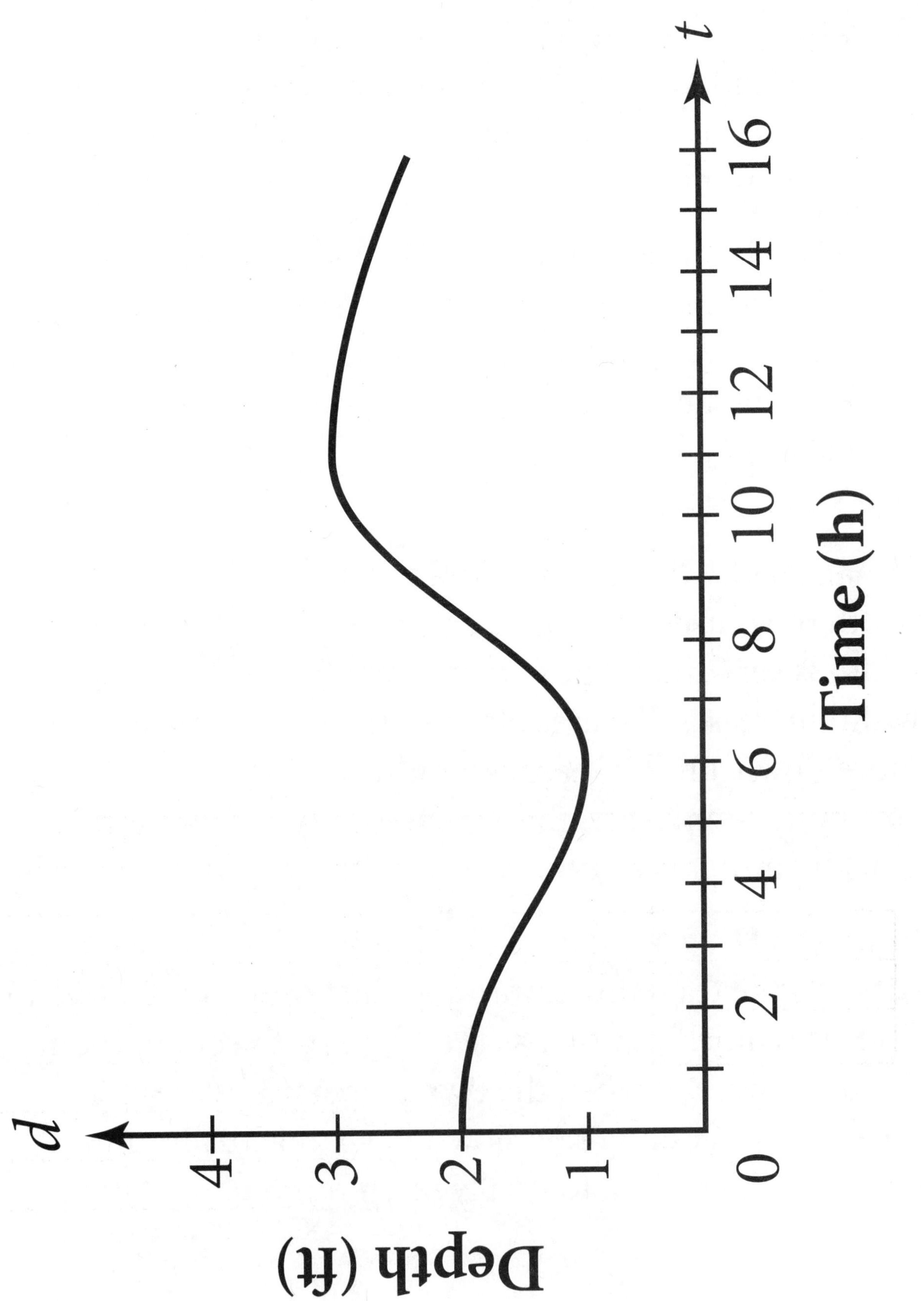

A Graphic Message

Name ______________________________ Period __________ Date ______________

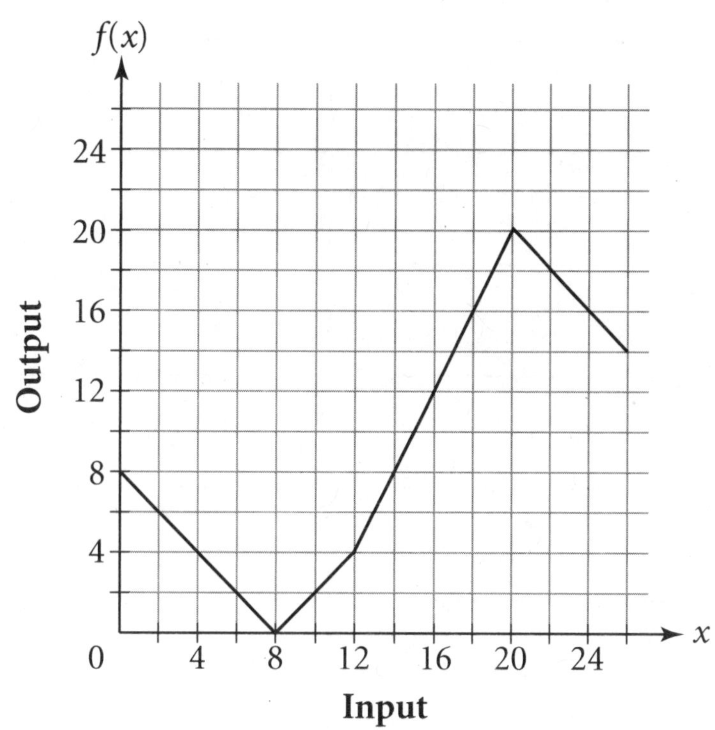

Notation	Value
$f(3)$	
$f(18) + f(3)$	
$f(5) \cdot f(4)$	
$f(15)/f(6)$	
$f(20) - f(10)$	

Notation	Value
$f(0) + f(1) - 3$	
$5 \cdot f(9)$	
x when $f(x) = 10$	
$f(9 + 8)$	
x when $f(x) = 0$	
$f(8 \cdot 3) - 5 \cdot f(11)$	
$f(4 \cdot 5 - 1)$	
$f(12)$	

Letter-Number Chart

Letter	Number
A	1
B	2
C	3
D	4
E	5
F	6
G	7
H	8
I	9
J	10
K	11
L	12
M	13

Letter	Number
N	14
O	15
P	16
Q	17
R	18
S	19
T	20
U	21
V	22
W	23
X	24
Y	25
Z	26

Pulse Rate Sample Data 2

88	76	84	64	60
64	60	64	68	74
68	68	72	76	72
52	72	64	60	56
72	88	80	76	64
72	60	76	88	72
64	60	60	72	92
80	72	64	68	

Moving a Quadrilateral

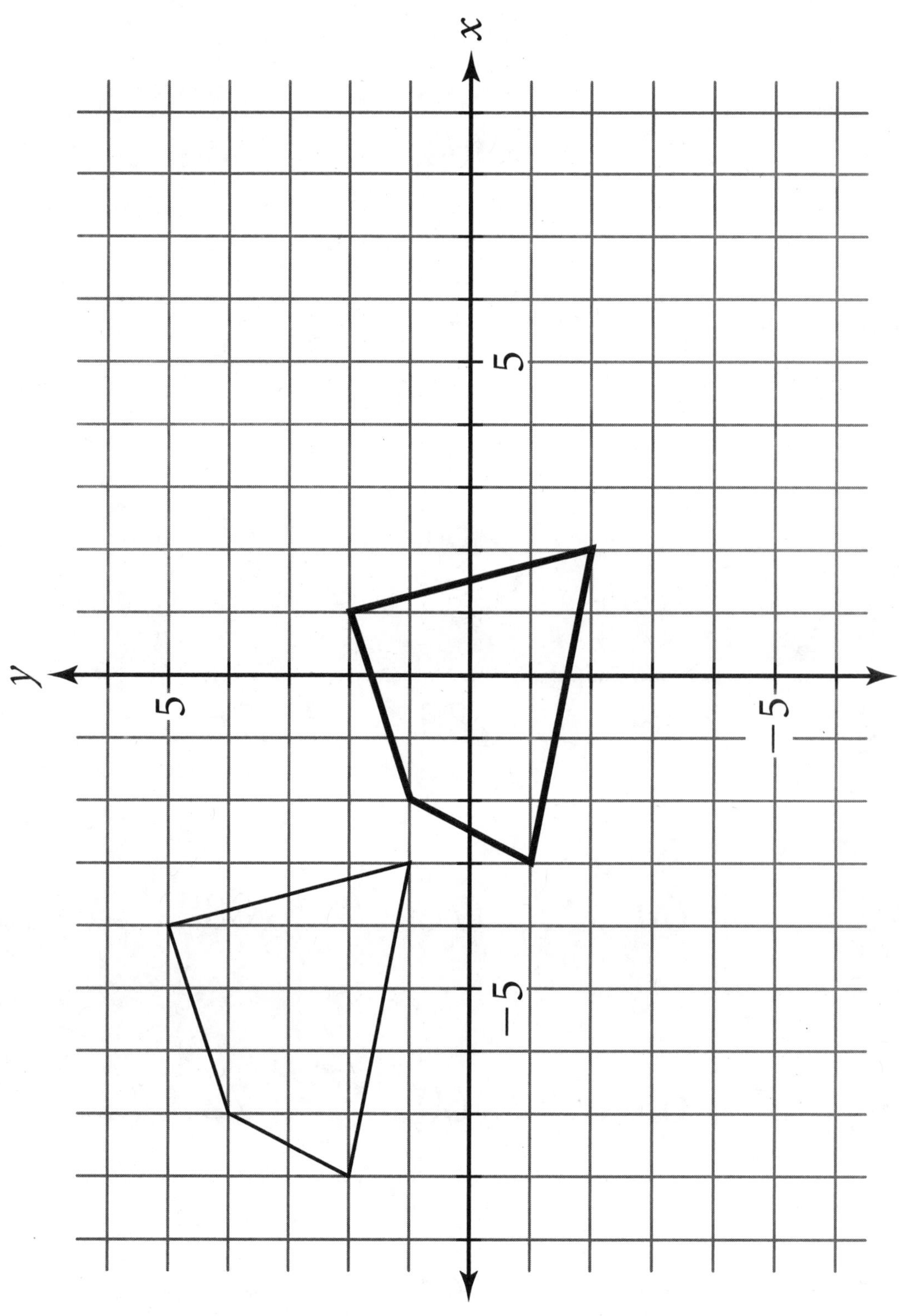

Moving Absolute Values

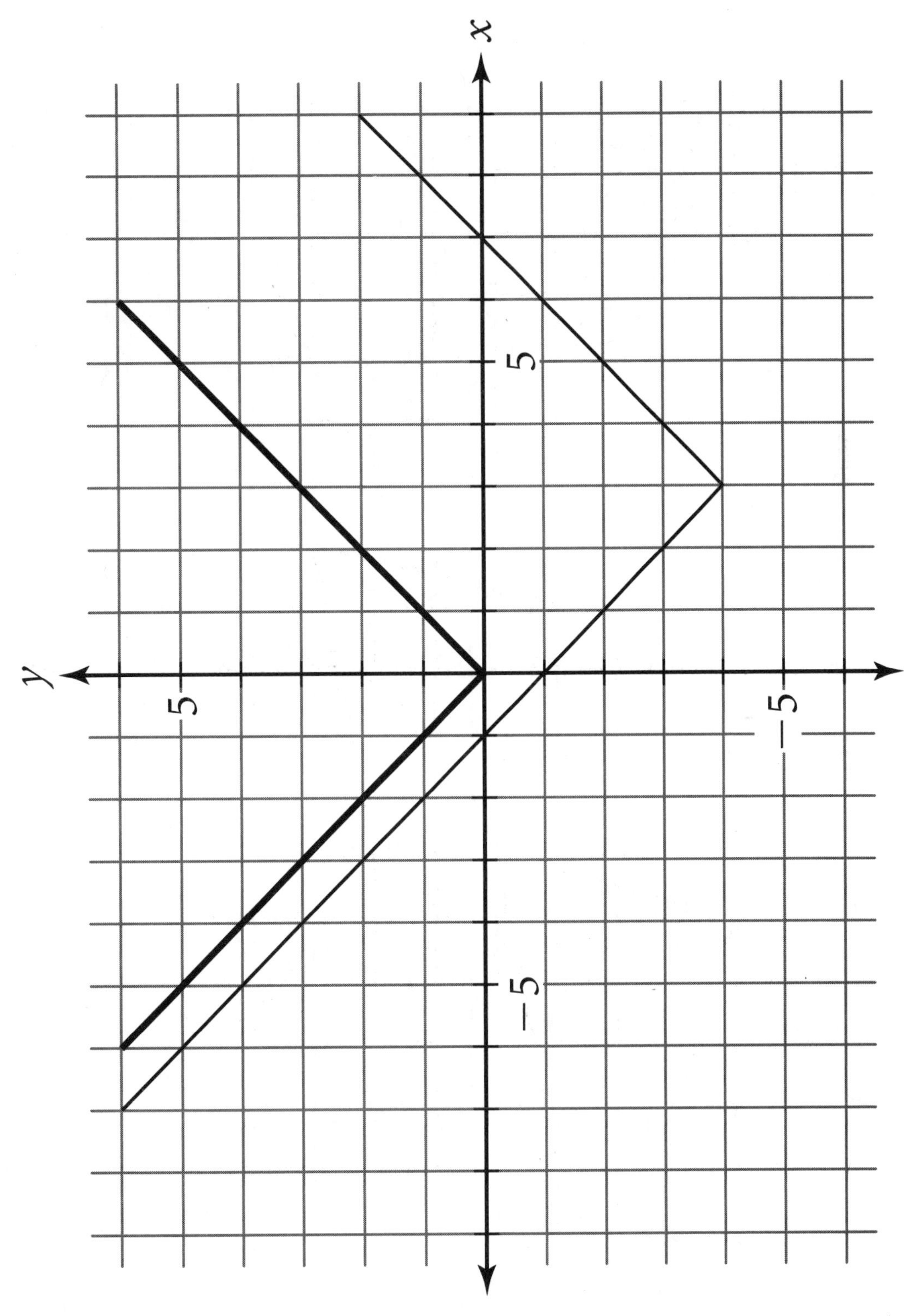

Flipping a Letter

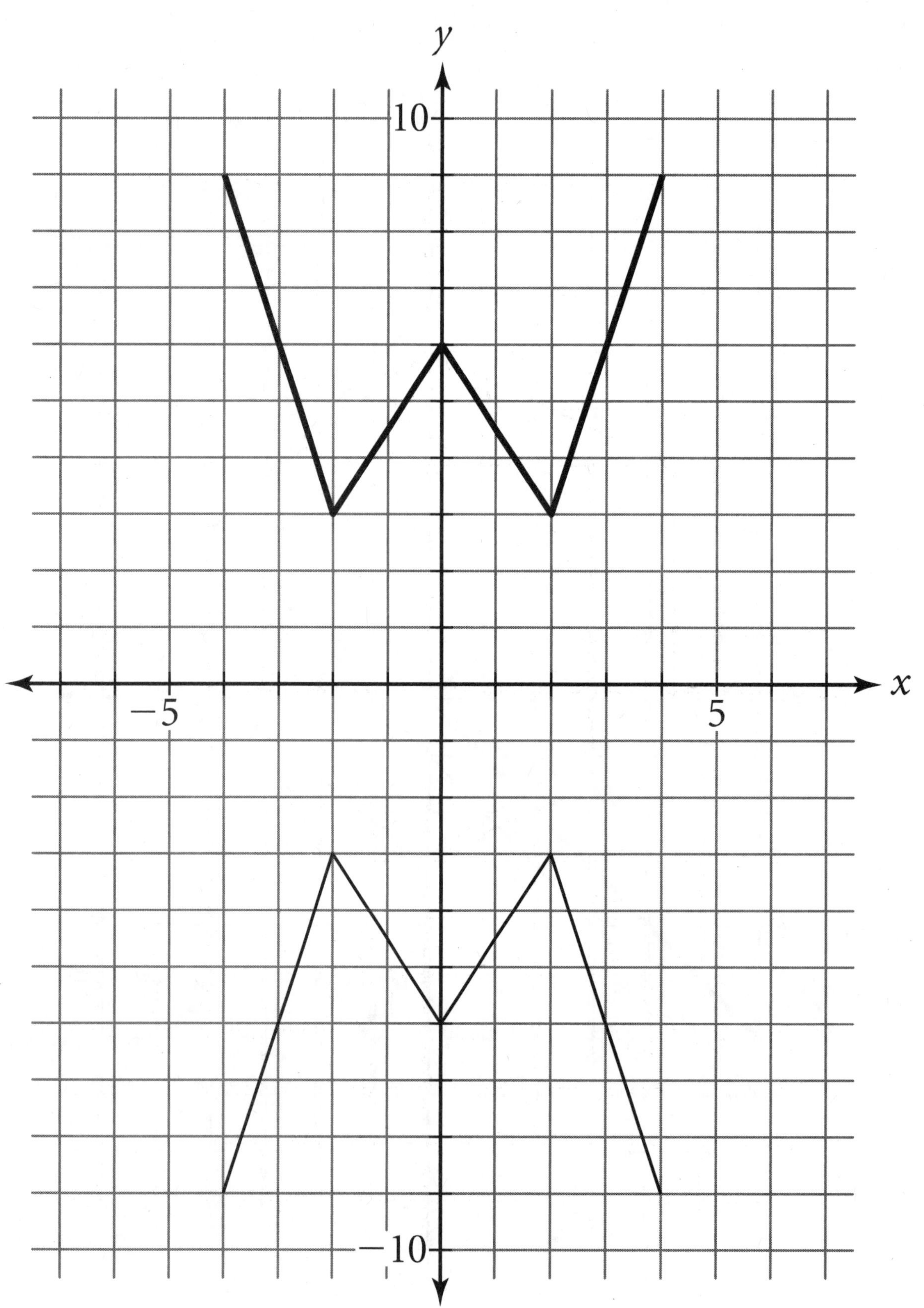

Stretching a Polygon

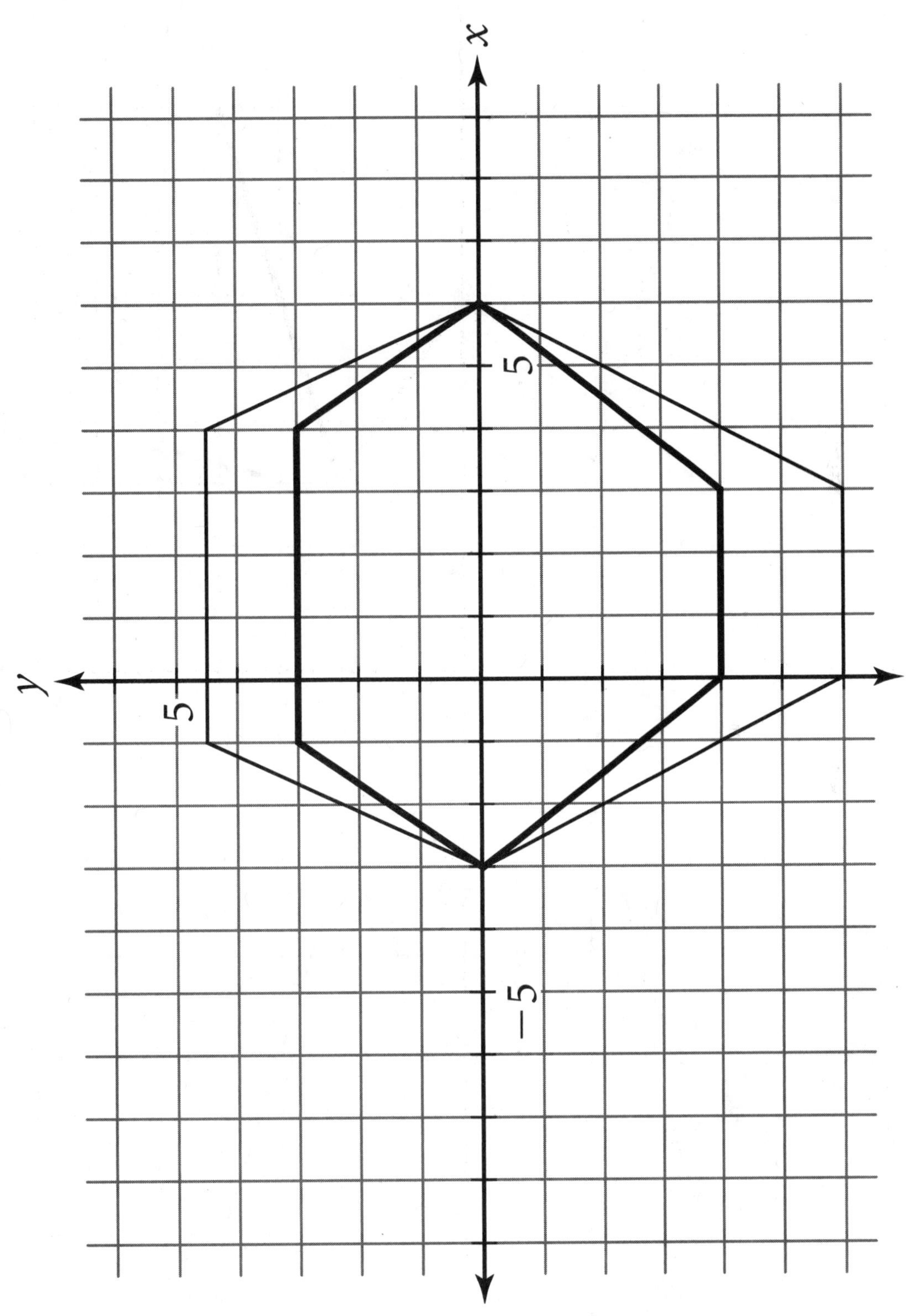

The Rolling Marble

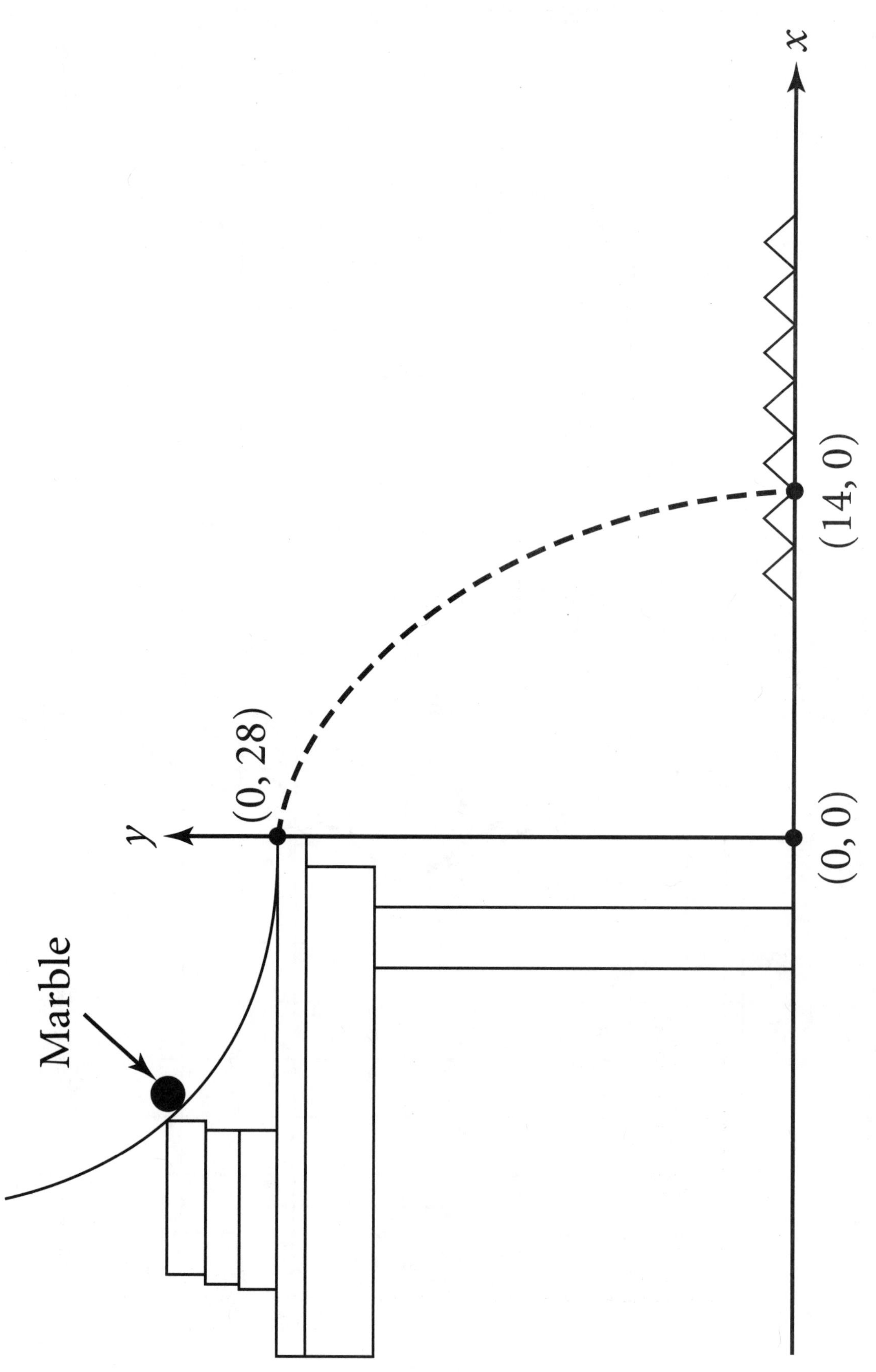

Number System Venn Diagram

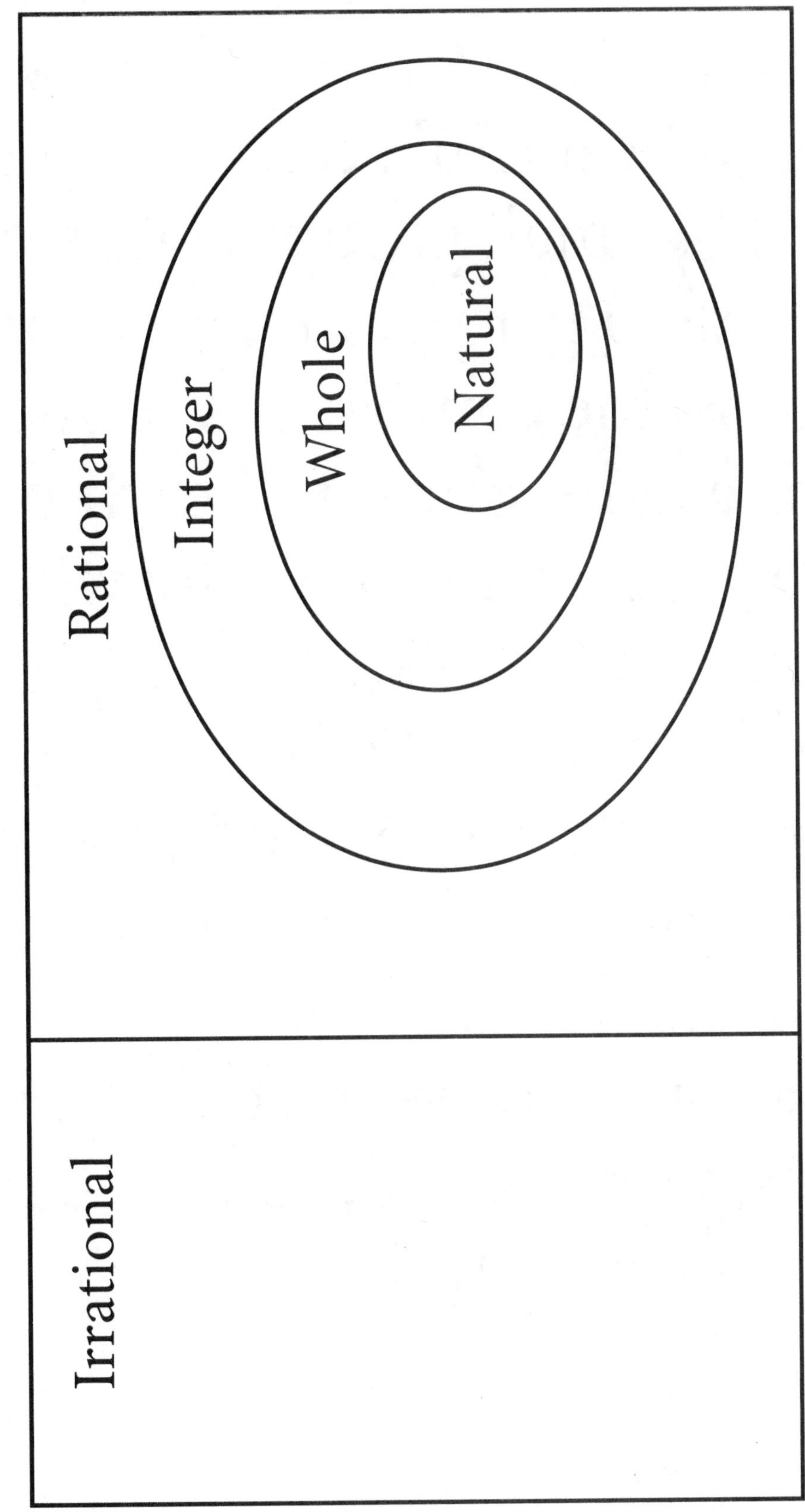

An excursion train that travels through beautiful scenery can be rented by small groups. The standard price is $50 per person. To promote business, the company is thinking of offering a discount: For each person in the group, the company will deduct $1 off the standard rental price per person. For example, a group of 20 people would pay only $30 per person. Running the train for an excursion costs $400. What limitations should the company place on the size of groups eligible for the discount?

The Quadratic Formula

$$ax^2 + bx + c = 0$$

$$ax^2 + bx = -c$$

$$x^2 + \frac{b}{a}x = -\frac{c}{a}$$

$$x^2 + \frac{b}{a}x + \left(\frac{b}{2a}\right)^2 = -\frac{c}{a} + \left(\frac{b}{2a}\right)^2$$

$$\left(x + \frac{b}{2a}\right)^2 = -\frac{4ac}{4a^2} + \frac{b^2}{4a^2}$$

$$\left(x + \frac{b}{2a}\right)^2 = \frac{b^2 - 4ac}{4a^2}$$

$$x + \frac{b}{2a} = \pm\frac{\sqrt{b^2 - 4ac}}{\sqrt{4a^2}}$$

$$x = -\frac{b}{2a} \pm \frac{\sqrt{b^2 - 4ac}}{2a}$$

$$x = \frac{-b \pm \sqrt{b^2 - 4ac}}{2a}$$

A stunt airplane at an air show was taking off when its pilot had to reverse direction to avoid hitting another plane. The stunt plane quickly changed direction again and resumed climbing, only to change direction again and begin dropping as part of a stunt. The stunt plane reversed direction at 5, 12, and 35 seconds after takeoff. Sketch a graph of the plane's rate equation.

Circle Graphs

Name ______________________________ Period ____________ Date ______________

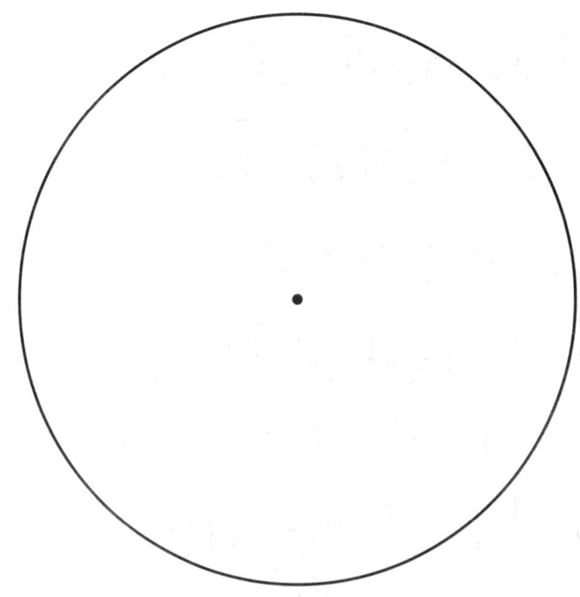

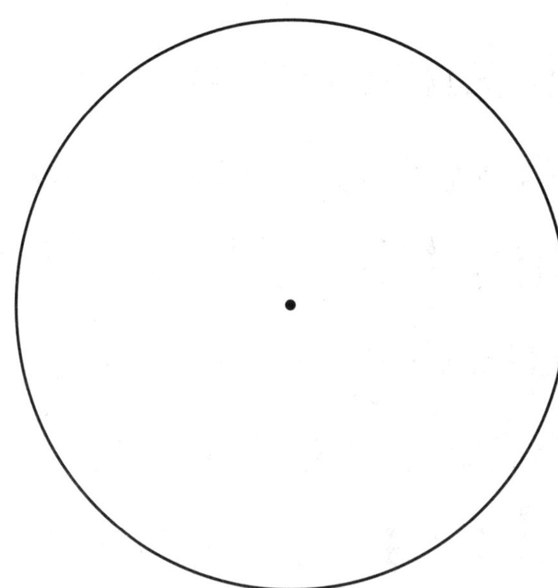

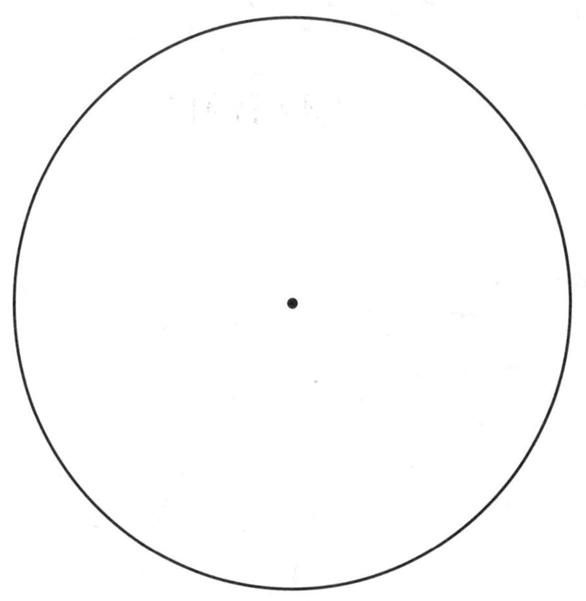

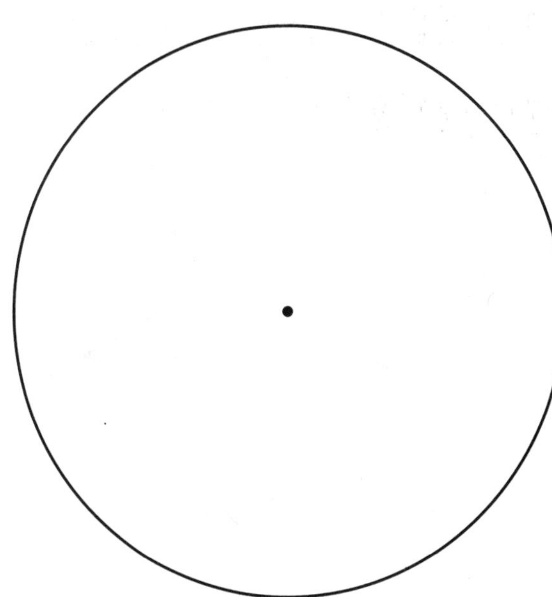

Casting Arrangements

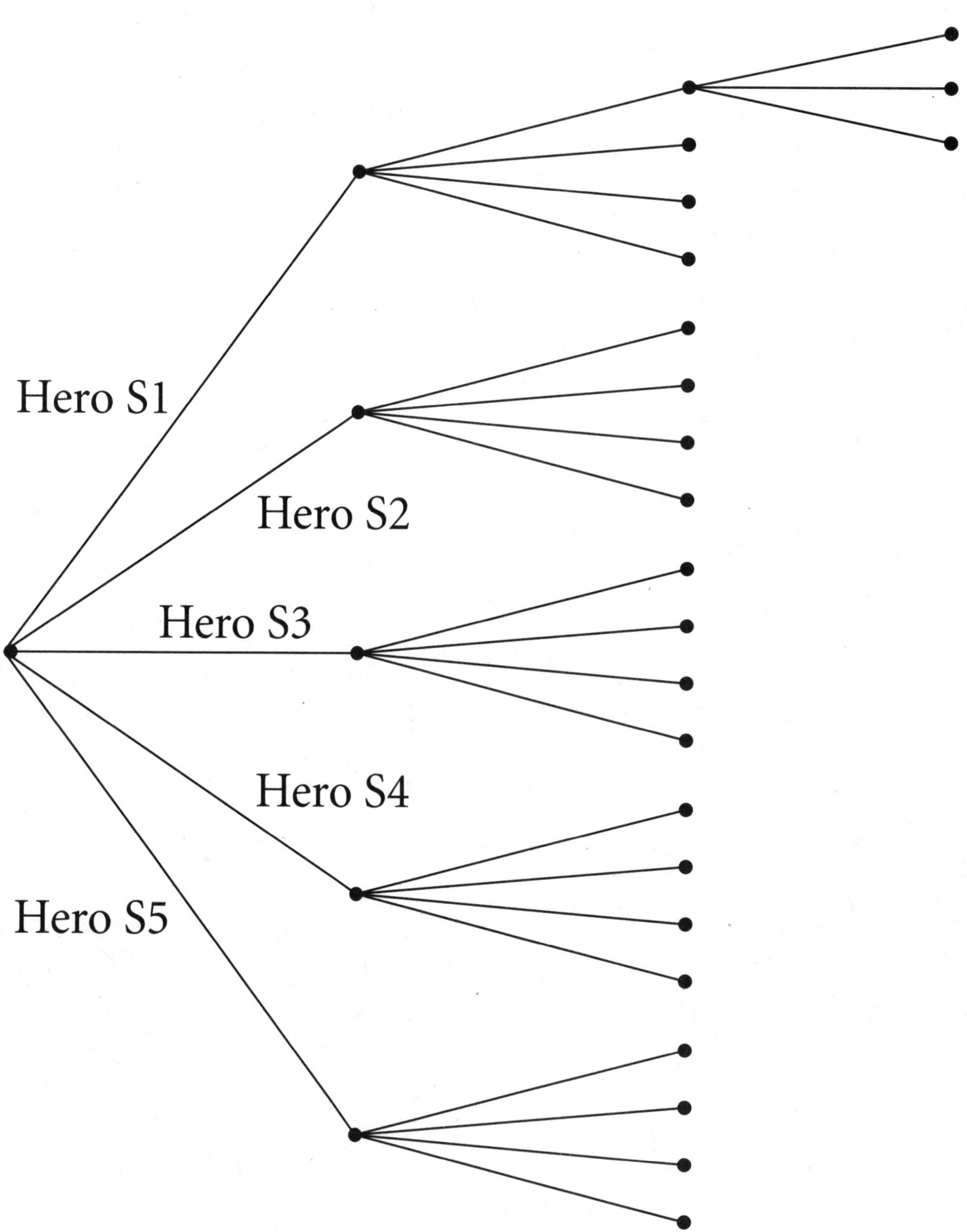

Pinball Game Sheet

Roll 1

Square

Round

Roll 2

Unit

Prime

Composite

Pinball Pupils

Experiment Totals

1st Roll 2nd Roll

S

Start total

R

S and E

S and O

R and U

R and P

R and C

Experimental Probabilities

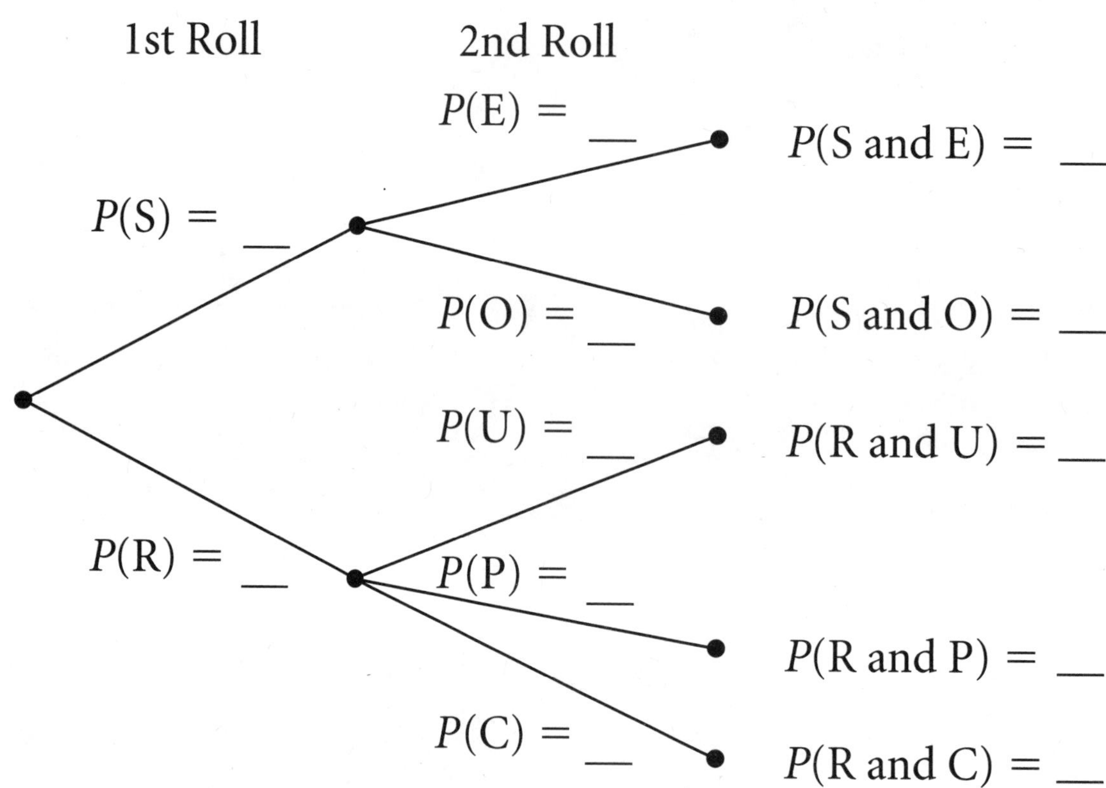

You are surveying a four-sided piece of land. From your Global Positioning System (GPS) you have found that one corner of the land is at a tree 638 feet due north of the corner that's next to a large rock. A third corner is at a post 138 feet south and 550 feet east of the tree. The fourth corner is at the edge of a pond. The rock is 400 feet west and 100 feet north of the corner by the pond.

Quadrilaterals

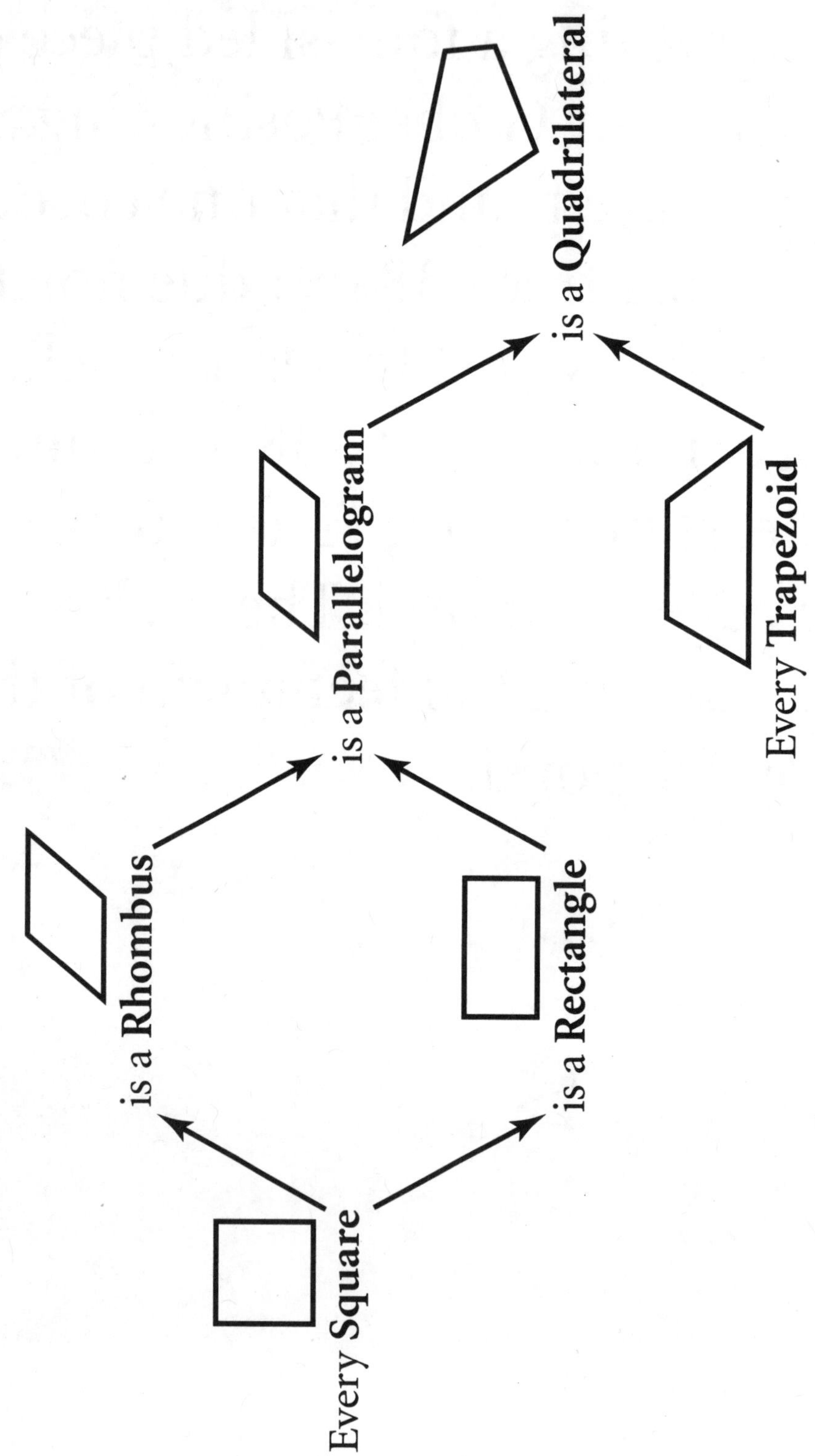

What's My Area?

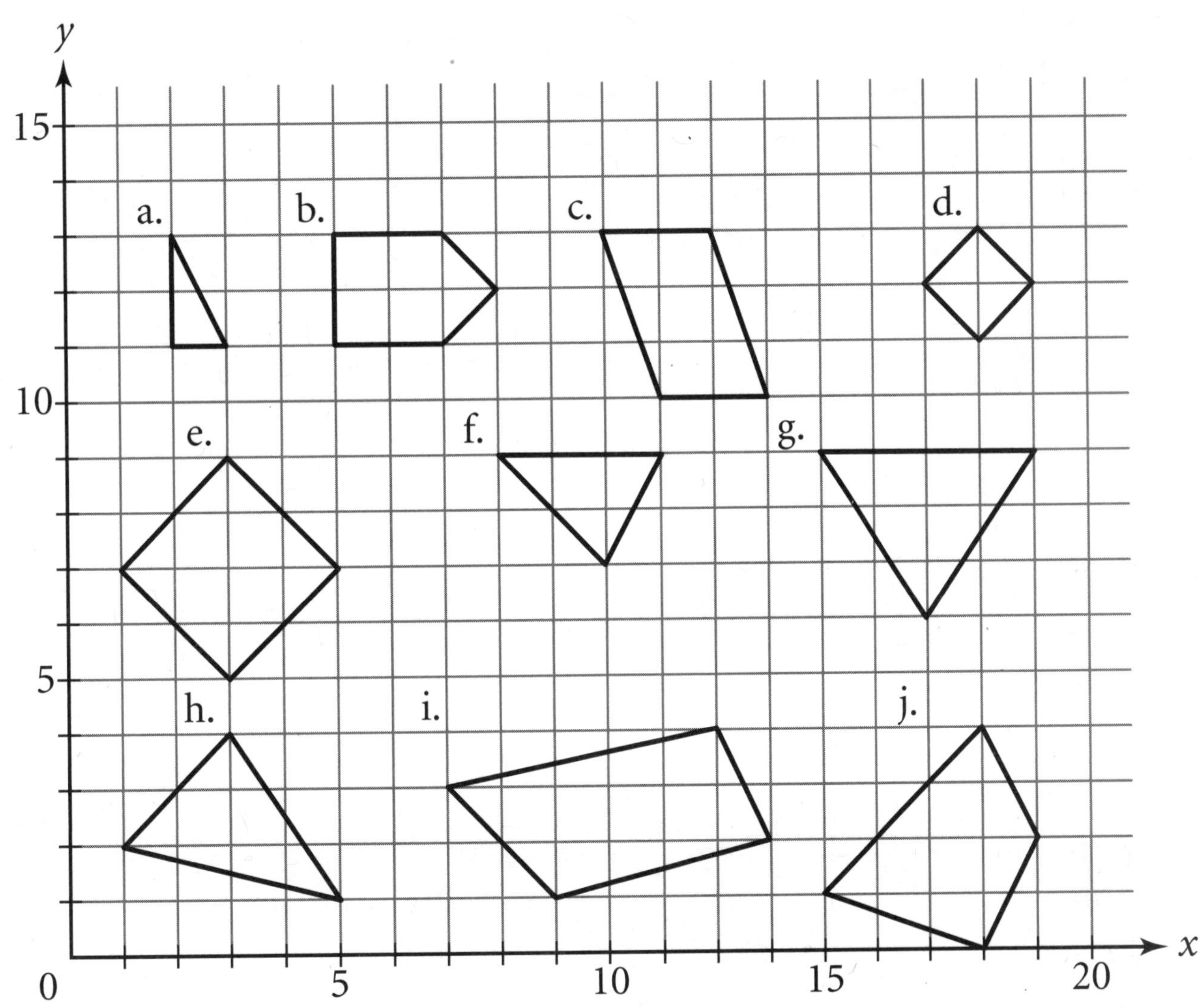

Pyramid Net

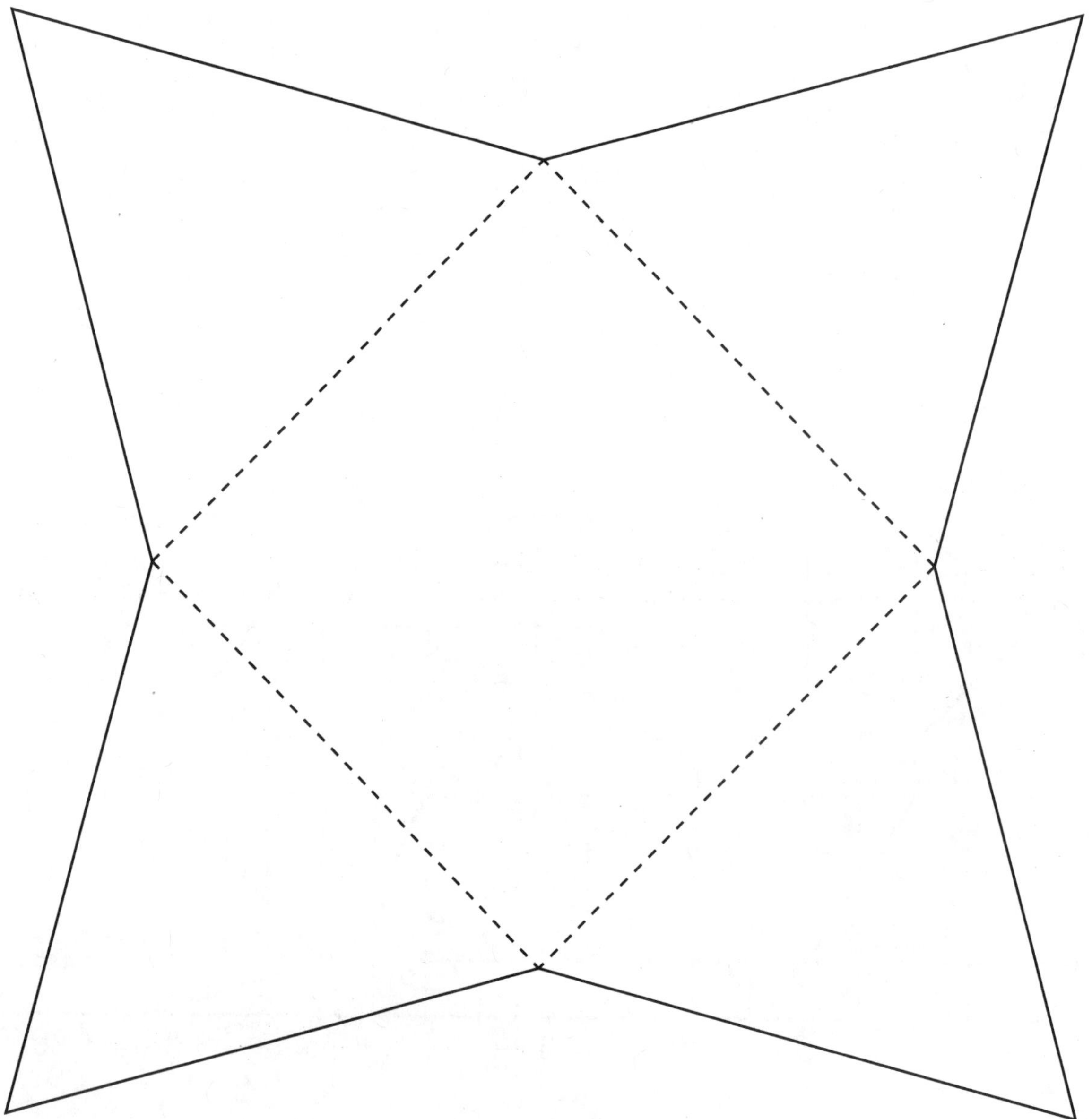

Amusement Park Map

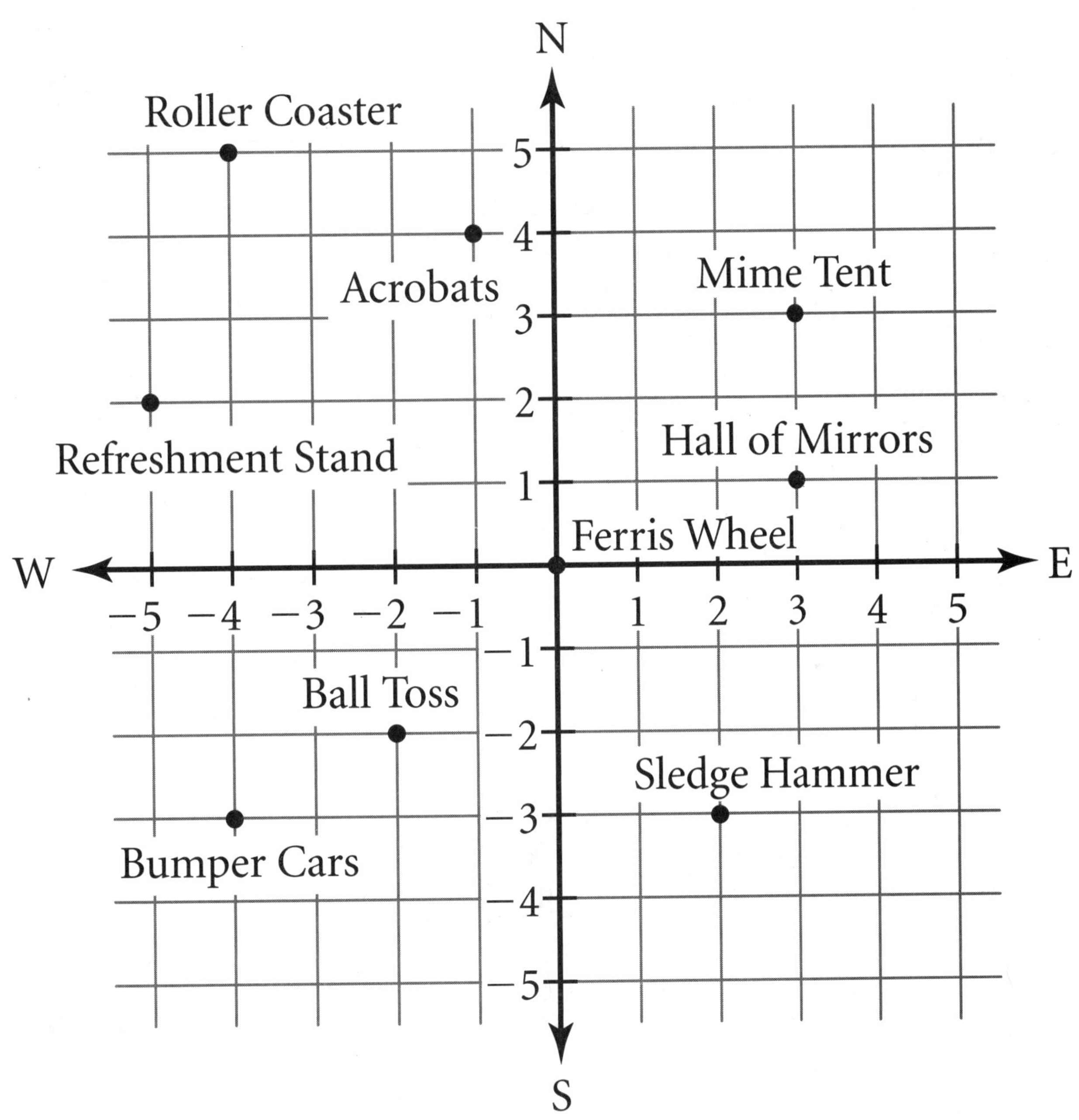

Earth and Moon

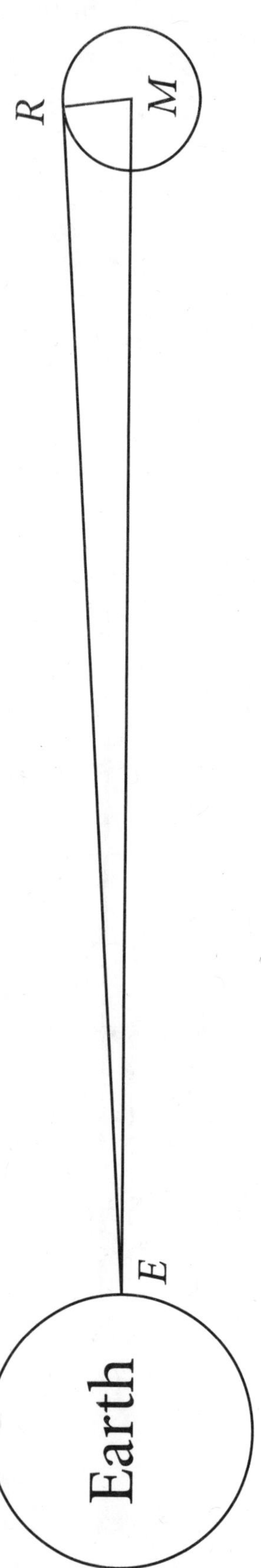

Contour Map

Name ______________________________ Period ____________ Date ______________

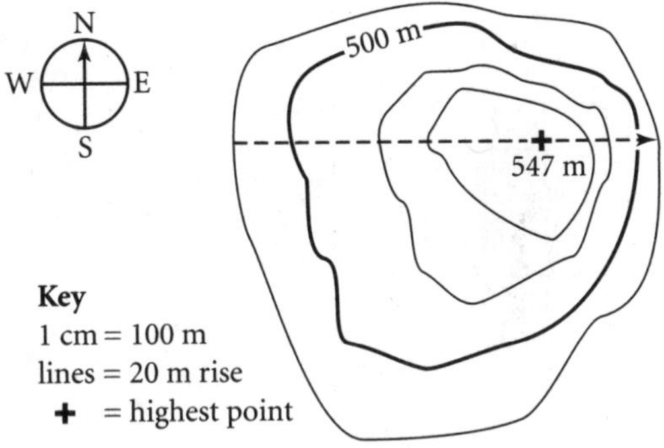

$\frac{1}{4}$-Inch Graph Paper

Name ______________________ Period __________ Date ______________

$\frac{1}{4}$-Inch Grids

Name ______________________________ Period __________ Date ______________

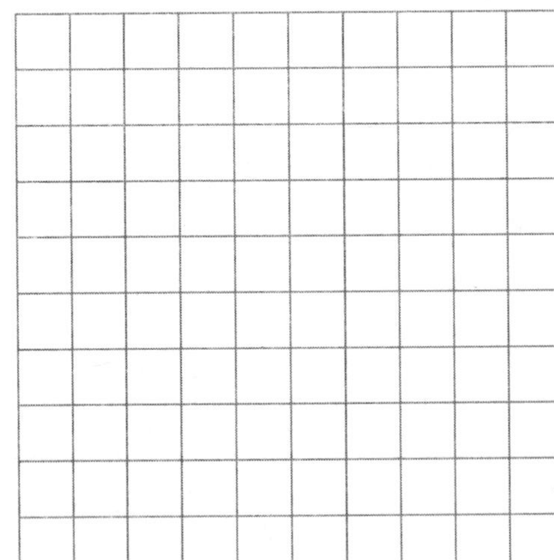

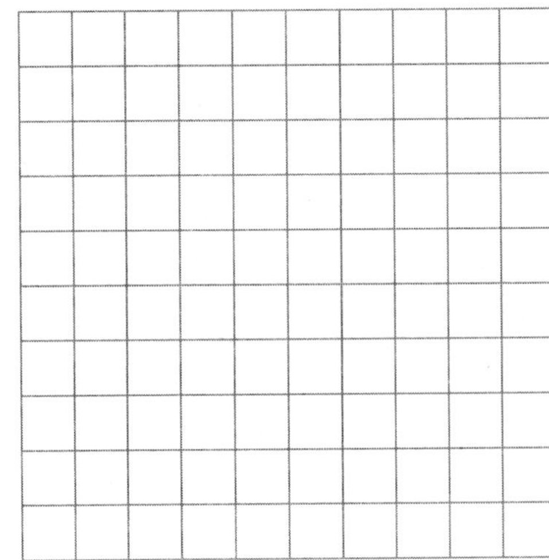

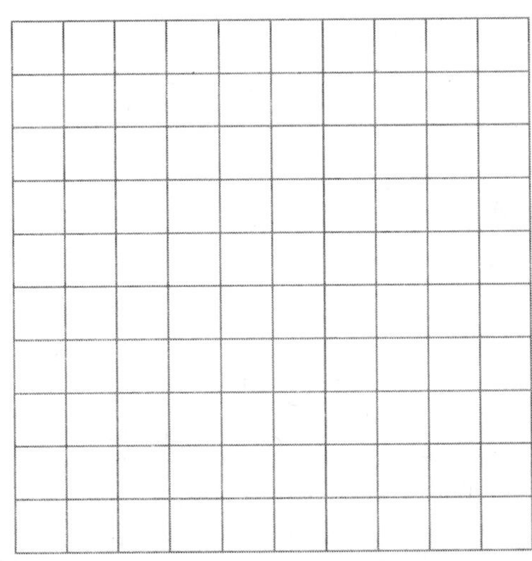

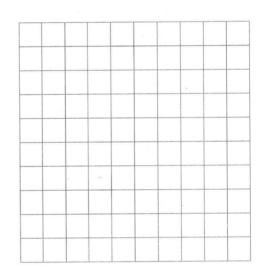

1-Centimeter Graph Paper

Name ______________________ **Period** __________ **Date** ______________

1-Centimeter Grids

Name ________________________________ Period __________ Date ______________

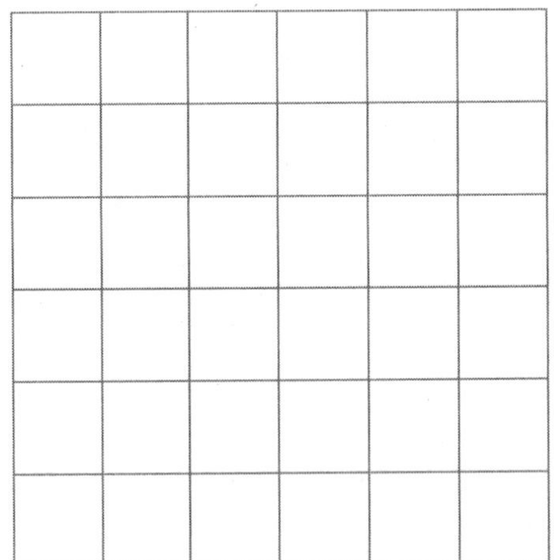

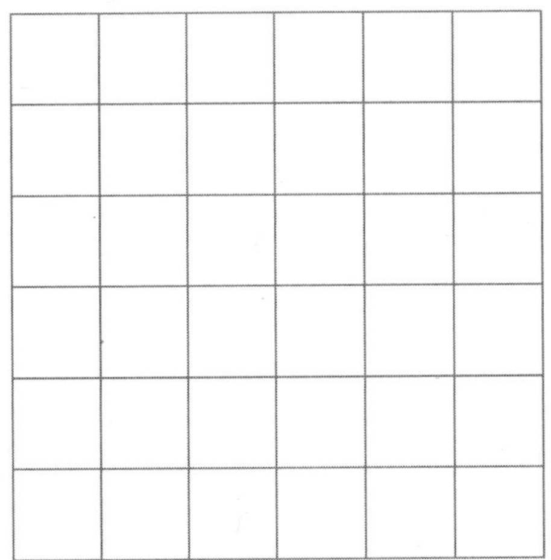

Comment Form

Please take a moment to provide us with feedback about this book. We are eager to read any comments or suggestions you may have. Once you've filled out this form, simply fold it along the dotted lines and drop it in the mail. We'll pay the postage. Thank you!

Your Name ______________________________

School ______________________________

School Address ______________________________

City/State/Zip ______________________________

Phone ______________________ Email ______________________

Book Title ______________________________

Please list any comments you have about this book.

Do you have any suggestions for improving the student or teacher material?

To request a catalog, or place an order, call us toll free at 800-995-MATH, or send a fax to 800-541-2242.
For more information, visit Key's website at www.keypress.com.

Fold carefully along this line.

POSTAGE WILL BE PAID BY ADDRESSEE

Attn: Editorial Department
1150 65th Street
Emeryville, CA 94608-9740

Fold carefully along this line.

Comment Form

Please take a moment to provide us with feedback about this book. We are eager to read any comments or suggestions you may have. Once you've filled out this form, simply fold it along the dotted lines and drop it in the mail. We'll pay the postage. Thank you!

Your Name ______________________________

School ______________________________

School Address ______________________________

City/State/Zip ______________________________

Phone ______________________ Email ______________________

Book Title ______________________________

Please list any comments you have about this book.

____

____

____

____

____

____

____

____

____

____

Do you have any suggestions for improving the student or teacher material?

____

____

____

____

____

____

____

To request a catalog, or place an order, call us toll free at 800-995-MATH, or send a fax to 800-541-2242.
For more information, visit Key's website at www.keypress.com.

Fold carefully along this line.

POSTAGE WILL BE PAID BY ADDRESSEE

Attn: Editorial Department
1150 65th Street
Emeryville, CA 94608-9740

Fold carefully along this line.

Comment Form

Please take a moment to provide us with feedback about this book. We are eager to read any comments or suggestions you may have. Once you've filled out this form, simply fold it along the dotted lines and drop it in the mail. We'll pay the postage. Thank you!

Your Name ______________________

School ______________________

School Address ______________________

City/State/Zip ______________________

Phone ______________________ Email ______________________

Book Title ______________________

Please list any comments you have about this book.

____

____

____

____

____

____

____

____

____

____

Do you have any suggestions for improving the student or teacher material?

____

____

____

____

____

____

____

To request a catalog, or place an order, call us toll free at 800-995-MATH, or send a fax to 800-541-2242. For more information, visit Key's website at www.keypress.com.

Fold carefully along this line.

NO POSTAGE
NECESSARY
IF MAILED
IN THE
UNITED STATES

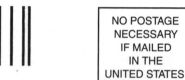

BUSINESS REPLY MAIL
FIRST CLASS PERMIT NO. 338 EMERYVILLE, CA

POSTAGE WILL BE PAID BY ADDRESSEE

Attn: Editorial Department
1150 65th Street
Emeryville, CA 94608-9740

Fold carefully along this line.